LAND OF THE HIBERNATING RIVERS

Life in the Arctic

LAND OF THE

HIBERNATING RIVERS

Life in the Arctic

T. A. Cheney

Illustrated with photographs

Harcourt, Brace & World, Inc., New York

PICTURE CREDITS

William Bacon from Rapho Guillumette: p. 93; T. A. Cheney: pp. 16, 30, 65, 110, 112, 112, 115, 116; Steve & Dolores McCutcheon: pp. 63, 72, 73, 75, 76, 78, 79, 81, 89, 97, 98, 103, 105; Novosti: pp. 7, 45, 53; Dolores D. Roguszka for Alaska Pictorial Service: p. 85; Bob and Ira Spring: pp. 61, 86, 88, 94, 96; Sovfoto: pp. 21, 29, 32, 35, 48; State of Alaska: pp. 90, 102; Tass: 5, 39, 46; Tass from Sovfoto: pp. 41, 56.

Harbrace maps

Curriculum-Related Books, selected and edited
by the School Department of Harcourt, Brace & World,
are titles of general interest for individual reading.

First Edition
Library of Congress Catalog Card Number: 68-13814
Printed in the United States of America

CONTENTS

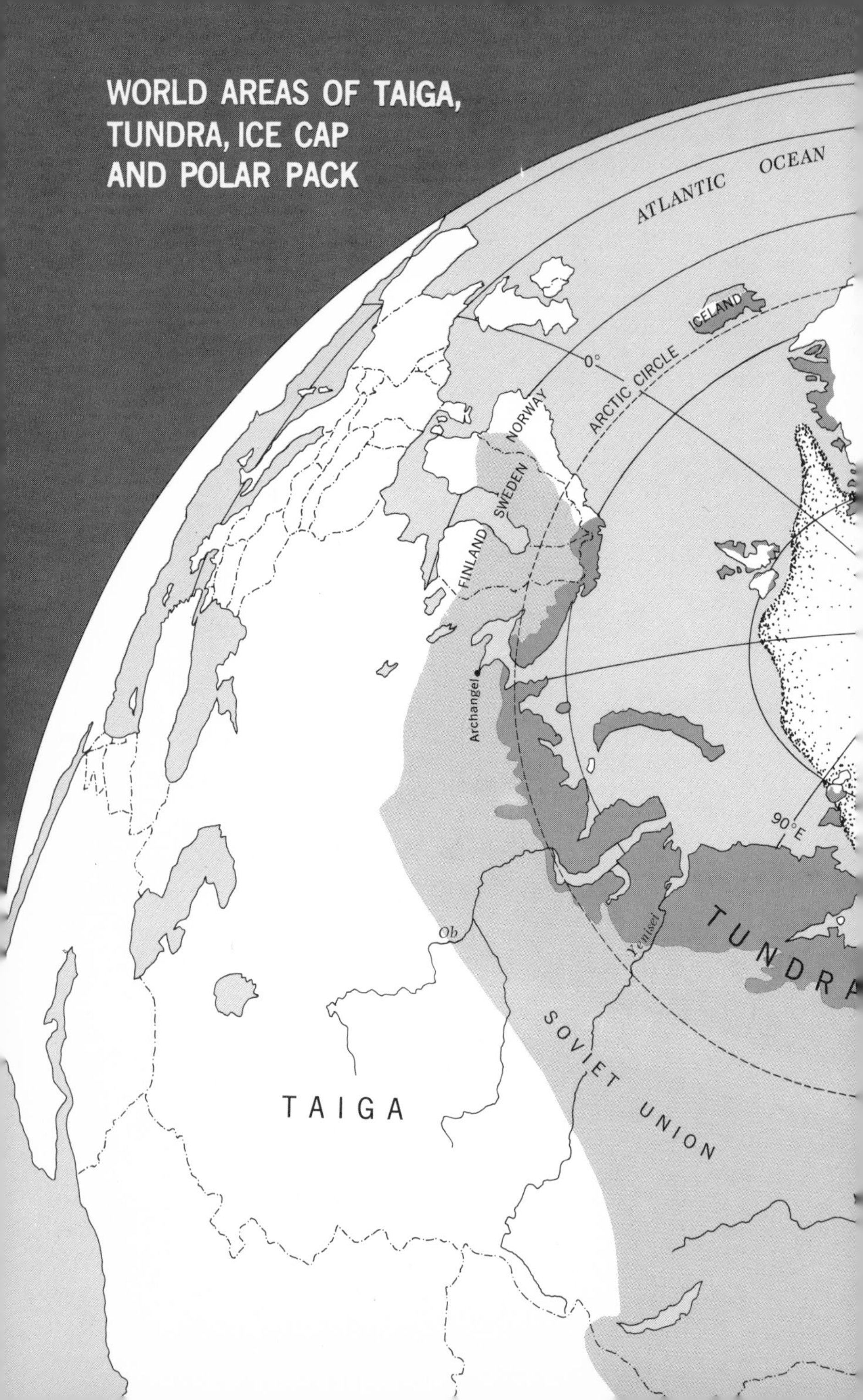
WORLD AREAS OF TAIGA, TUNDRA, ICE CAP AND POLAR PACK
ATLANTIC OCEAN
ICELAND
0°
ARCTIC CIRCLE
NORWAY
SWEDEN
FINLAND
Archangel
90°E
Ob
Yenisei
TUNDRA
SOVIET UNION
TAIGA

EWFOUNDLAND
TAIGA
HUDSON BAY
90° W
Fort Churchill
TUNDRA
CANADA
U.S.A.
Mackensie
RTH POLE
POLAR PACK
TUNDRA ANALOG AREA
ALASKA
Anchorage
80°
Kivalina
Yukon
70°
66 2/3°
TAIGA ANALOG AREA
ARCTIC CIRCLE
erkhoyansk
BERING SEA
60°
PACIFIC OCEAN
Magadan
50°
SEA OF OKHOTSK
180°

WORLD AREAS OF TAIGA
ATLANTIC OCEAN
NEWFOUNDLAND
TAIGA
CANADA
HUDSON BAY
Fort Churchill
Churchill River
ICELAND
NORTH SEA
50°
60°
70°
90°
0°
66 2/3°
ARCTIC CIRCLE
Bergen
NORWAY
SWEDEN
FINLAND
Archangel
BAFFIN ISLAND
DAVIS STRAIT
GREENLAND
ELLESMERE ISLAND
SPITZBERGEN ISLANDS
NORTH POLE
FRANZ JOSEF LAND
ARCTIC OCEAN
NOVAYA ZEMLYA
OSTROV OKTYABARSKOY REVOLYUTSII
TUNDRA ANALOG AREA
YUKON TERRITORY
Juneau
Yukon River
Fort Yukon
ARCTIC SLOPE
Fairbanks
Nenana
Barrow
Anchorage
KENAI PENINS
ALASKA
Kivalina
Kotzebue
Nome
CHUKCHI SEA
WRANGEL ISLAND
CHUKCHI PENINSULA
Ob River
Dudinka
Norilsk
Igarka
Yenisei River
LAPTEV SEA
NEW SIBERIAN ISLANDS
SOVIET UNION
TAIGA
Lena River
TAIGA ANALOG AREA
Verkhoyansk
VERKHOYANSKI KHREBET
CHERSKI KHREBET
BERING SEA
Yakutsk
Magadan
KAMCHATKA PENINSULA
SEA OF OKHOTSK
SAKHALINE ISLAND
PACIFIC OCEAN
TAIGA ANALOG AREA
Yana River
Verkhoyansk

TAIGA

It is difficult to imagine a place of such dramatic contrasts as the vast World Taiga. Mosquitoes and black flies are in clouds thick enough to drive a man insane in July's 90-degree temperature. Yet within several months the temperature will have dropped as much as 180 degrees and hardly a creature will be stirring in the bleak winter darkness. In spite of these extremes, however, many thousands of people and many different kinds of animals have found ways to survive and live quite happily in this strange region.

LOCATION

Taiga (tie-gah′) is a Russian word used by all geographers and foresters to refer to the world's great northern forests of evergreen trees. The World Taiga extends from Scandinavia to the Pacific coast of the Soviet Union and from Alaska to Newfoundland. Its southern boundary is at about 60° north in western Europe, but drops to about the 50° latitude in eastern Siberia and swoops down from northern Alaska to about the Great Lakes. Some geographers call just the northern edge of the forest, taiga; whereas others refer to taiga as the entire belt of evergreen forests in the northern latitudes. This book will compromise and call the taiga the northern half of the great *boreal forest*, where the trees begin to grow shorter and scragglier.

The forest of this Arctic environment gives its name to the whole region, taiga. The Soviet Union has the largest taiga regions but there are broad areas of taiga within Scandinavia, Canada, and Alaska. Taiga makes up about one third of the entire world's forests.

Since it would be impossible to discuss here the entire World Taiga with all its minor variations, one representative part, or *analog area*, has been carefully selected to concentrate on. When something is very similar (although not identical) to something else, one says it is *analogous* (an-al-o-gus). One can also say that either of the two things being compared is the *analog* of the other. When geographers want to state the idea that certain geographic areas are similar, they say that these are *analogous areas*, or more simply *analog areas*.

The analog area chosen to exemplify the World Taiga is in eastern Siberia, lying almost entirely within the watershed of the Yana (Yah-nah) River. The southern boundary is the Arctic Circle and is bisected by the 133°00′ E. longitudinal line. The western edge is cut by the Verkhoyanski Khrebet (Varecoy-yahn-ski Krreh-be). The word *khrebet* appears fairly often in this book and on many reference maps; it simply means "mountain range." This particular khrebet comes south from the Arctic Ocean, tracing a graceful series of S-curves which are faithfully paralleled by the

A tributary of the Lena River

Lena (lay-nah) River. The Lena is one of the world's largest rivers, and her 12,000 square mile delta in the Arctic Ocean is the third largest in the world.

WINTER

Most people have heard that Siberia is a terrible place to be in the winter. This is not an exaggeration. The eastern part of Siberia, even below the Arctic Circle, has the coldest winters of the civilized world. The town of Verkhoyansk has an *average* January temperature of 57 degrees *below* zero. The temperature frequently drops far beneath even that terrifying figure; the lowest recorded degrees in that town was –89°F.

This general area has been called the world's "cold pole." Temperatures in the Antarctic continent frequently drop even lower, but the big difference is that only "hardy, heroic explorers" brave the Antarctic winters, whereas ordinary people live and work in the winters of Verkhoyansk.

There are practically no plants or animals living on the land of the Antarctic continent, but there are trees, flowers, animals, and people living in Siberia. The reason that nothing grows well in the Antarctic is not so much that the winters are too cold, but that the *summers* are too cold. In Siberia, however, the summers are warm enough to account for the enormous difference between these two refrigerated lands.

When people hear cold words like Arctic, winter, and Siberia, they are also apt to think right away of snow. One would expect Siberia to have great, paralyzing depths of snow. Many people picture children and parents all bundled up in rabbit-fur robes while being pulled rapidly through great, tall drifts of snow by three, nostril-steaming, black horses. These pictures, however, are of winters in Leningrad and Moscow several thousand miles west of the part of Siberia we are discussing. Here, along the river Yana, the carpet of snow for the entire winter may be only 10 inches deep.

It is not unusual for many parts of the United States to have 10 inches of snow fall in one storm. Yet Siberia, where the temperature is down around –60°F much of the time, gets only 10 or 12 inches of snow in a year. Central New

A girl can hear her neighbors a mile away

York State, which no one would call "Arctic," normally receives about 100 inches per year, ten times more than Northeast Siberia.

Another climatic element one might expect to find in Siberia is a howling wind. Wrong again. Most of the winters along the Yana feel no wind at all. When the winter wind does blow, it rarely goes faster than 3 or 4 miles per hour—hardly enough to flutter a flag. The average January wind speed is about one mile per hour.

This combination of frigid temperatures and calm air does strange things to sounds in the air. The sound of ice in a pond crackling and rumbling as it freezes and expands on a cold night is as shattering as gunfire. The sound of a sled on crusty snow can be heard for several miles. One could easily listen in secretly on his next-door neighbor, even though the cabin might be a mile down the trail. The howl of a husky can be heard for miles and miles through the dense, cold air.

Low wind speed means that people can stand the cold winter temperatures more easily. A person feels warm or cold because of how fast his body heat is taken away from him. The faster the wind, the faster the heat is taken away. If there is no wind to carry away body heat, a man feels no colder at –50°F than he would at 0°F with a wind snapping the warmed air away from his skin. Probably most people still will not want to go swimming during January, but at least it is not really as bad a place to live as it first sounds.

SPRING

Spring in many places of the world is the time during which great changes happen, usually over a period of about 60 to 90 days. The change from snow to jonquils may be great, but it is gradual. Here, along the Yana, the changes are even greater, and they are certainly not gradual. Everything goes from winter to summer in 30 days. The average temperature around the first of May is apt to be still below freezing, but by the first of June it is up around 57°F. (That is as warm as the warmest month of the year in San Francisco.) Such a rapid change in temperature causes a springtime explosion of life.

It is fortunate for this part of Siberia that there is not

much snow to melt. Imagine the frightful floods there would be in Central New York if its deep cover of snow melted as quickly as the snow in Siberia. The rapid melting of Siberia's 10 inches does cause them great difficulties, but of a different kind. Most of their transportation for the six or seven months before the spring thaw has been on sleigh trails over the hard-packed snow. Suddenly, there is nothing but mushy, slippery slush through which nothing moves.

After the slush has turned completely to water and run off into the streams, the local people are still in for more trouble. Now the melted soil is so full of water that every trail has become an impassable route of slippery, oozy mud. No vehicles can move for weeks from the time of snow thaw until the ground water has slowly seeped from the soil to the streams.

The other form of precipitation to be concerned with is rain. A place like New York City receives about 40 inches of rain per year. Reno, Nevada, which geographers consider a desert, receives about 8 inches. This portion of Siberia receives even less, about 5 inches. Where the Yana empties into the Laptev Sea, the annual precipitation is down to about 3 inches. There are few places in the world that receive less rain and snow.

If there is so little rain, even less than some deserts, isn't it strange that there are such forests in Siberia? This plant growth is possible because of an unusual combination of natural elements. In a normal desert the soil is almost always bone dry, and it is important that plants have water available to them during the spring growing season. In Siberia, however, the ground water is held in place all winter long by being frozen as ice crystals between all the tiny grains of soil. In the spring it melts into life-giving water.

Because the trees and plants need water for growth in the spring, it is important that it rain in the fall. It is this fall rain that becomes the frozen reservoir in the soil. There is great difficulty in summers when it has not rained enough during the *previous* fall. Except for the little bit of water made available by the melting of the snow, there is not enough soil mositure for healthy growth and any attempts at agriculture without irrigation are doomed to failure.

SUMMER

By July this fascinating country has warmed up to an average of 59°F, and during the summer, temperatures higher than 90°F are not unusual in Verkhoyansk. It is this warmth and the fact that the sun is shining for so many hours per day during the growth season that account for the completely different world here from that at the South Pole. The difference between the coldest and warmest temperatures recorded in Verkhoyansk is 181 degrees, the greatest annual difference in the entire world.

PERMAFROST

An extremely important result of very low winter temperatures is that all moisture in the soil and rocks freezes solid.

Some of it has not thawed in thousands of years. Geographers call this frozen condition, *permafrost.*

Permafrost can be found over some 5 million square miles of the Arctic and Subarctic. It is not just "there," the way moose and mice are "there"; it controls and dictates the entire way of life for all plants and all animals, including man.

If there were no permafrost, things would be so different that one would hardly recognize the area. If trees and plants had to depend only on the summer rainfall, they could not survive. Probably, it would be a true desert of ceaselessly shifting sands.

Most people are familiar with the kind of frost that occasionally surprises everyone and kills or ruins millions of dollars worth of fruit, but here we are talking of frost that deeply penetrates the soil and stays there for months at a time. Anyone in the northern latitudes who has had to dig a hole in January, knows how rock-hard the soil is at that time of year. This frozen soil extends downward to different depths, depending upon what part of the world it is in. In this section of Siberia, the soil and rock are frozen solid down to a depth of 500 or even 1,000 feet.

The top few feet of this permanently frozen ground thaws during the summer and is called the *active layer.* The rest apparently never thaws. If the active layer stayed frozen, certain building problems could be avoided.

A cabin built above permafrost frequently sinks in one corner—the corner where the stove is. The secret of successful building on permafrost seems to be to keep the frozen soil frozen. Insulation is packed under cabins to prevent the active layer from thawing. Some buildings have been designed so that cold air can blow in under them all during the winter because foundation walls allow a little bit of heat to seep down and melt some of the frost—a little bit more each year. In the summer the air holes are plugged up so that no warm air can blow in under the buildings.

Most people know that when water freezes into ice it takes up more space. A bottle of milk left out on the doorstep over a cold night will freeze and force the milk up out of the top as it turns to ice. There simply is not enough space left in the bottle any more.

When water freezes and expands in soil it causes everyone a lot of trouble. Highways can be pushed up just as easily as the milk from the top of the bottle. Small and large buildings alike can be lifted up in the fall and dropped back down in the spring. This moving around is not the best thing in the world for buildings. Walls develop cracks, pipes break, and chimneys fall down.

A person would know for certain that he was in permafrost country if he saw a cabin filled with ice up to the roof and if there were frozen waterfalls draping down from each window and from cracks in the roof. The cause of such a weird sight is easy to understand, but certainly strange.

One must first have a mental picture of what is happening under the ground in these cold regions. In August or September, when the active layer of soil has thawed, but before the air temperature has begun to average below freezing, the ground resembles a sandwich.

The first two or three feet of soil is completely filled with water so that it is a sea of mud, down to a surface that is frozen solid. This is the top of the true permafrost. It is solid for perhaps hundreds of feet further down. When winter begins, the active layer starts to freeze again and it does so from the surface downward. After a few weeks of freezing there is a kind of water sandwich. There is a slice of frozen soil on the top, which is perhaps a foot or two thick. The second slice is at the bottom (the top of the true permafrost). In the middle of the sandwich is a great deal of water.

The water touching the top of the permafrost freezes gradually, as does the water touching the frost layer above. As this freezing into ice goes on, there is less and less room, which means that the remaining water becomes pressurized. Water under pressure is a powerful force. If, for example, there happens to be a cabin nearby whose stove has kept the ground under it unfrozen, the water under pressure will go to that weak point and blast through. It occasionally goes right up into the cabin and flows out on the floor. If there is enough water and enough pressure, it will actually fill up the house and explode it. This is not a fairy story; it has happened many times in permafrost country.

Russians call this water *Naled* (nailed) water. Sometimes the naled water will find another outlet, such as a weak spot caused by digging along a new highway or railroad. In this case, the naled water will flood out over the highway or railway, and the ice may build up many feet high and completely block traffic when the water freezes. Ice is not an easy thing to get rid of either. Even explosives do a poor job. The ice simply bends with the blast.

The only way to protect homes, highways, or other heavy structures is to somehow keep the ground frozen all year long. The Russians have experimented with keeping the inside of an earth dam frozen by running pipes through it, carrying a salty water that is cold enough to freeze the surrounding soil. The liquid will not freeze itself because salt water does not freeze at 32 degrees.

Most buildings in the Arctic regions are insulated at the bottom, not so much to keep the building warm in winter but to keep the soil below from thawing from heat escaping from the floor and from warm summer temperatures. Some higher buildings must be supported by steel columns instead of walls. These columns cause no difficulties in most parts of the world, but in the frigid regions they may carry heat from the building deep down into the permafrost. Some buildings in the permafrost region have their columns refrigerated to prevent this thawing action.

Manmade structures are not the only ones affected by the alternate freezing and thawing of permafrost. The entire landscape of our Siberian region shows the effects. Often the naled water will cause the ground to heave or bend upward like a blister. Occasionally there will be whole fields of these blisters, or mounds. Usually they are between 2 and 5 feet tall and only a few feet across, but sometimes they grow as high as 50 feet. There are even some that have grown several hundred feet tall and look like a normal, low hill. These hills are known as *pingoes* (ping-goes) in the taiga of North America.

As these features grow they tend to crack open at the top and the naled water may seep out. It may also blast out and look for a while like a geyser, raising great clouds of vapor. The vapor is caused by the difference in temperature between the unfrozen naled water (around 32 degrees) and the air temperature (perhaps 80 degrees lower). This is the same process that turns your breath into a visible vapor when you exhale on a cold day.

When a number of neighboring mounds split open, allowing the water they contain to flow out, there can be a field of ice as thick as 15 feet covering hundreds of acres. These are called *naledi* (nail-dee) fields by the Russians, or *ice fields* by North Americans.

Another effect upon the landscape caused by the active layer of the permafrost is what the Siberian people call *The Dancing Forest*. This refers to trees that are seen growing at strangely tilted angles, frequently in the same direction. The trees begin by growing in a perfectly normal way on level ground but are forced upward and outward by the unfolding of an ice blister below them. As the mound grows upward the trees on the sideslopes are tilted farther and farther over.

MOUNTAINS

The Yana analog area is outlined by high mountain ranges (khrebets). Their heights have been seen by few, and most have never been climbed by modern man. The Verkhoyanski Khrebet is tallest in its southern parts, with peaks as high as 8,000 feet above sea level. The line of the mountain ridge divides the rainfall into rivers which flow either west into the Lena or east and north into the Yana.

The rivers on the west side are roaring mountain streams that cut deep, steep-sided canyons as they rush to the level flats of the Lena. Along the Lena toward the Verkhoyanski

Permafrost created this Dancing Forest

Khrebet, there are several vertical cliffs rising over 1,500 feet, straight up.

If someone managed to scale this high cliff he would expect to be in the midst of Alp-like mountains, but in actuality it would not look that way at all. The eastern slope toward the Yana River is very gentle, compared to the extremely steep western slope. The area between them is what geographers call the Yana Plateau. This plateau is a high, rolling plain lying between the Verkhoyanski Khrebet on the west and another mountain range to the east called the Cherski (chair-ski) Khrebet, with occasional peaks rising to 10,000 feet.

This highland is technically a plateau, but it is far from being a level plain. The plateau is covered with rounded hills and a great number of flat-topped hills. The entire plateau slopes gradually to the north, the Yana flowing gently down its center. There are rapids where the river crosses some particularly strong rock such as granite, but it is easy-flowing most of the way.

MINERALS

No one knows very much about the minerals in this region around the Yana. It remains not too well-known because it is such a difficult place to get to and even if valuable minerals were discovered today, it would be very expensive to mine them and transport them out. The taiga throughout the world suffers from the same problems. The taiga of Canada and Alaska has many known mineral deposits. Some are mined now, if they are very valuable, but many must lie there until some practical means of mining and transport can be worked out.

The Siberian taiga has been explored to some extent, and deposits of coal have been found in many places. The Russians estimate they have 460 million tons of coal within the taiga, 60 million tons of which are around the mountain town of Norilsk. A short railway hauls the coal down to the port of Dudinka on the Yenisei River. Ships go down the river to the Arctic Ocean and deliver coal all along the arctic coast.

Zinc, lead, and tungsten are said to abound near the Yana, although no large mines have yet been opened. Gold is found in the Cherski Khrebet to the east of the Yana and on the Chukchi Peninsula in the far northeast corner opposite the taiga of Alaska. Oil is found on the Arctic coast at the mouth of the Yenisei. Gas is presently being produced south of the Yana River area, just north of Yakutsk.

The Russians have high hopes that these are but small beginnings of a big future in oil and gas for Siberia. Siberia needs its own production of these important fuels if it is to develop economically. Most oil now has to be brought at great expense from the island of Sakahline in the Far East or from the fields in the southwest. Either way, the cost is limiting the economic development of eastern Siberia.

SOILS

The soils of an area usually make up one of its most important resources and yet it is the one most overlooked by the average person. In Arctic areas, however, the soils are not as economically important as in many other parts of the world. They would be more important if they were fertile, but they are not.

Unfortunately, even if they were good, fertile soils, agriculture would still be limited by the climate and the permafrost. In fact, the main reason the soils are not very good is that they are frozen most of the year—and always have been. Soils improve with age. They start out as rocks which gradually break down into smaller and smaller grains of minerals. Rainwater then seeps down through the top layers carrying tiny bits of minerals and pieces of grass and twigs until finally the soil is a fertile mixture of clay, sand, silt, and plant parts. Turning rocks into fertile soil takes a very long time and it takes much, much more time if the soil is frozen ten months out of twelve.

Although soil scientists (*pedologists*) have not studied the soils in the Yana River area very much, they do know that they are mostly of the *gley* type. Gley soils are a bluish-gray, unbelievably sticky clay. The soils become gley because during the two months when they are unfrozen, they are always water soaked. The water from the melted permafrost cannot go down because the permafrost below remains frozen solid. The soil just sits there and gets slimier and slimier, summer after summer. If someone walks in it, the gley sticks to the sole of his boots. Then gley sticks to gley until each shoe weighs about 10 pounds and has to be scraped off.

VEGETATION

Such water-logged clay soils under such harsh climatic conditions are not very good for growing crops. Agriculture is only an experiment in this part of Siberia. Some towns on the Lena River have grown vegetables outdoors, but the best hope seems to be for growing things in hot houses. The extremely long, sunny days make plants grow to great sizes, seemingly overnight. Outdoors, only the taiga forests are able to maintain themselves in the two short summer months.

Unlike the forests of warmer lands, the taiga has very few different kinds of trees. Along the Yana, there are mostly larch trees. Although the larch can grow almost anywhere, it prefers the slightly higher and drier ground. It avoids growing on land too near the river, which is flooded every year. Trees grow on the slopes of the Verkhoyanski Khrebet and other ranges up to the elevation of about 3,500 feet above sea level. Above that elevation the trees become shorter and scragglier until, finally, there are no trees at all and the tops of the mountains have only grasses and short plants.

Down in the valleys the few larches are joined by Balsam poplar trees and Korean willows, which grow better on this moister ground. The best Korean willows grow straight and tall (up to 60 feet) and are used for building bridges and as telegraph poles. The larger poplars are felled, hollowed out, and used as canoes by the local people.

There are hundreds of thousands of square miles of this dull forest comprised of larch trees with moss underfoot.

The silent taiga forest

People who have been alone in it have described it as gloomy, mournful, silent, and forbidding. It is so silent in the taiga forest that a Russian poet has said that to tread there is to know fear.

The only break in the monotony of the taiga comes from an occasional, treeless bog or swamp. A stranger to the taiga might run out happily from the frightening forest into the openness of a bog, only to find that the forest had been safer. If the bog happened to be a *quaking bog* he would be in for a horrible surprise, if not a drowning. A quaking bog is a mat of grasses floating on water that is often deep. It looks wet, to be sure, but it looks like ordinary wet, swampy ground. A stranger might walk around for a while just thinking the "ground" terribly mushy, until he stepped on a weak spot and shot right down through the grassy, floating mat into the cold, black water below.

Another strange danger in the Arctic areas of the world is *pond porridge.* This is the polite name given to a slimy mass by Canadian scientists working at the border between the taiga and tundra at Fort Churchill on Hudson Bay. Floating on the ponds during summer are small orange colored clumps of algae, fungi, and bacteria, held loosely together by pieces of grass and twigs. These slimy rafts gradually sink to the bottom and deposits pile up year after year. After hundreds of years go by, the pond is gradually filled in.

After the porridge builds up high enough, the summer drought exposes the top to the drying action of the sun. The surface of the orange-colored material turns a very light gray and gives no warning of the slime below. A man once jumped from the top of an Army tank down onto what looked to him like dry, hard sand. He sank in so deep that as he was being saved he was pulled right out of his boots. His boots are still there to worry some hard-digging scientist in the year 2069. Reindeer are never seen going across these pond porridge areas. If one is ever out in this kind of country, he should follow the reindeer trails. The trails may wind around, but they will always be on the driest, firmest ground.

RIVERS

More important than bogs and other minor forms of surface waters are those major features called rivers. Any geographical area of the world derives much of its personality from the presence of rivers—or their absence. As transportation systems, rivers have played a large part in the development of any country through which they run. This has been true, too, of the taiga, but in a negative way. The rivers of the taiga have prevented the rapid development of the north country for several reasons, the most important of which is that most major rivers of the World Taiga flow north—away from civilization.

The history of Russia and, indeed, the world, would be quite different if the rivers flowed southward, bringing water to the dry expanses of this nation and providing easy transportation of natural resources from the vast regions of the Arctic and Subarctic. As it is, the rivers run north and out into an ice-choked sea through which ships move only with great difficulty—even when preceded by giant ice-breakers such as the nuclear-powered *Lenin.*

The Lena River, which runs close to the western boundary of the Yana analog area, is born far to the south and high above Lake Baikal's western shores. When the mountain snow is melting in the warm rains of April and May, the northern portion of the Lena is still frozen. This means that the warmer water from the south is flowing into the colder water of the north.

The Yana River has a different personality because its birthplace is not so far south. It has its beginnings in the Verkhoyanski Khrebet where not much snow or rain falls. Before the Yana ever begins to melt and flow in the spring, the Lena is already carrying the warmer water of the southern spring into the land of winter. The Lena becomes a scene of spring floods of monstrous character, whereas the Yana never floods.

The flooding of the Lena is the result of the difference in water temperature between the place of its birth and the neighborhood where it dies. Perhaps the best way to picture this changing character from south to north, is to follow an old birch log that has fallen into the Lena and is drifting down north. The birch tree was felled on the east bank of the Lena down south where the sun is warm, the younger birches are budding, the birds are flittering about, and all the snow has melted high in the hills. The Lena is being fed by this melted snow, the spring showers, and the melting permafrost. The birch log bobs along the surface of the Lena's waters, now a beautiful blue under cloudless skies.

As the white birch bobs closer and closer to the Arctic Circle things begin to change. The skies are just as blue, even bluer, but the air temperature has dropped all along the way. Where the log first tumbled into the stream, the mid-day temperatures were well above 50°F. Now, as it floats peacefully further north, the air is not yet above freezing. The snow has not melted; the permafrost in the soil has not melted; the ice in the little brooks is still firm; and there are no spring showers in this north country.

The Lena is still frozen solid. There is no place for the birch log and its water to go except on top of the ice. As the slightly warmer waters from the south flow on top of the ice, the ice begins to melt, crack, and float up to the surface. The rushing waters pick up these huge blocks of ice and carry them northward on top of ice not yet melted.

Everything is fine until the huge blocks reach a narrow place where hills come down close to each side of the river. The blocks and the birch log get caught, along with other logs ripped from the banks, and a dam of ice and wood is rapidly piled up. A lake then forms behind the dam and floods into the valley. Because the air temperature is still below freezing, the flooding water that covers the land to the sides of the main channel will freeze solid. As the air temperature begins to rise, a month or two after the warmer waters first arrived, the dam will finally break and allow the now rapidly melting river ice to flow on to the Arctic Ocean.

people in the area can take fish during the long winter. These unfrozen spots are called *polynyas* (polly-knee-ahs).

ANIMALS

One might expect that a forest as large as the Siberian taiga would be just about overrun by wild life. Such is not the case. Perhaps they dislike the gloomy, silent taiga as much as men do. Animals tend not to live in the deep woods, but near the occasional open places. There is a bit more food in such places and certainly a lot more company.

These open areas, many caused by numerous forest fires, attract such animals as foxes, lynxes, hares, timber wolves, and brown bears. The larger open areas and the lakes attract the Siberian moose, ermines, geese, and various flying, biting insects. The moose is being studied and experimented with in Siberia to see whether it can be domesticated. This great beast is an excellent source of meat and is eagerly hunted by people in Siberia, Canada, and Alaska. One moose will provide meat for an entire family for months. If herds of these huge animals could be handled, it would certainly ease the food problems of the far north. The moose could also be an excellent pack animal, suited perfectly to the unusual natural environment of the taiga.

The higher mountains around the Yana are inhabited by the great snowshoe rabbits and the occasional wolverine, whose fur is so prized by the local people as a ruff around their parka hoods.

Although one hears much about the trapping of beavers,

A frozen ice bridge

ermines, and sables, and exciting stories of shooting great brown bears, the most valuable fur-bearing animal in Siberia today is the fur squirrel. When a Siberian man goes hunting he may shoot a lynx or a bear while he is out, but his objective is to shoot as many squirrels as he can. Most of this hunting is done in the winter when the furs are better.

Summer in the Subarctic brings an onslaught of mosquitoes—droves and droves of mosquitoes. They crawl into a person's ears, eyes, nostrils, and even into his throat with the food he is eating. When a man lives for days and days with clouds of mosquitoes, there swells within him a certain helpless feeling of being smothered by soft wings.

There are some ways for a person to protect himself: he can wear tightly woven cloth, so that stingers cannot go between the threads; he can tuck his trousers into his boots and his tightly cuffed sleeves into gloves; he can wear a net that hangs down from a wide-brimmed hat and is drawn tightly around the neck. These precautions give good protection from the bites, but remember that the temperature may be in the 80's.

The only hope for even temporary relief is a windy day. The mosquitoes will not venture out of the woods if there is even a light wind. Since the woods are a wind-break one must get out into an open area to get the blessed relief of a breeze. This partly explains why the animals also like to live near an open area in the taiga. Even an animal as heroic as the moose is driven almost out of his mind by the hungry hoards of mosquitoes. Moose will swim to the middle of a lake to get away from it all; they will even go into a village if it seems to provide relief from these terrible torturers.

It is the female mosquito who does all the biting. Nature has arranged things so that she must have a meal of blood if she hopes to lay any eggs. Since her egg-laying drive is very strong she will go to any length to find that one blood meal.

During July the mosquito troops are joined by the attacking forces of the tiny black fly, a minute monster who seems to be nothing but a pair of flying teeth. Also taking part in the invasion are the flying bulldogs, or *tabanid* (tah-bah-nid) flies. These are related to horseflies, but some are much larger. Three or four of these bulldogs will adopt a

A man must protect himself against swarms of mosquitoes

Yakut children attending school

person for an hour or so and whirl at great speeds in tight orbits around his head. They blast right through his personal cloud of mosquitoes, knocking them left and right. Life during the time when all the flying, biting insects are active together is an experience one cannot forget.

HUMANS

Perhaps only time will tell which of the many species of animals now inhabiting the earth will be shown to be the most important, but one likes to believe that man holds that position. Human population within the World Taiga is very sparse, anywhere from 1 to 25 people per square mile, and the Yana River area is no exception. There are European Russians within the area, but they comprise less than 10 percent of the population. Most Russians live in Verkhoyansk and surrounding villages.

The majority of the permanently settled populace within this area is of *Yakut* (yah-coot) ancestry. The Yakuts are most influential in the region and yet they do not seem to belong. Their Yakut language is a Turko-Tatar language because they were driven here centuries ago from Central Asia where Turkish influence is heavy. In recent years the Soviet government has tried to bring the Yakuts into the heart of Soviet life, while still trying to allow them to retain their own language. Some schools teach in Yakut, but the majority of higher grades are taught in Russian because most available textbooks are in the Russian language.

The Yakut people are traditionally, and remain, horse and cattle keepers and breeders, but some prefer to keep reindeer and follow the nomadic life. These and the Asiatic tribes of Lamuts are known as the "people of the reindeer." There are about 33,000 Lamuts and their fellow tribesmen, Tungus, within all of Siberia and 236,000 Yakuts. Other reindeer keepers live to the northeast of the Yana River area, in the tundra. These are the 12,000 Chukchi who are more closely related to the Eskimos of Alaska, Canada, and Greenland.

All people must adapt to their environment. There is, in fact, a science called *ecology* (ee-coll-o-gee) that is concerned with the relationships between organisms and their environments. Since in the study of any geographic area one must be concerned with ecology, there will be frequent references made to the various *ecosystems* within the Arctic and how they affect each other. An ecosystem is a combination of life forms, the natural environment, and the activities man performs in order to survive within the overall system. Each of these human activities can be considered an *ecosystem link* connecting man with his environment and thus creating an ecological system, or ecosystem.

Here in the taiga five ecosystem links cover almost every basic activity in which man must participate to derive the greatest number of benefits from his surroundings: *food and water*; *shelter, clothing, and fuel*; *communications and transportation*; *society and government*; *commerce and industry*.

FOOD

Since the availability of reindeer meat is crucial to man's survival, one must first consider what, in turn, is crucial to the life of the reindeer. The main foods for reindeer are *lichens* (like-enz), mosses, and in the summer, grasses and leaves. The most important food, lichens, grows very, very slowly. Their growth is about four to eight hundredths of an inch during an entire year. If a herd grazes across a field of lichens in the wintertime and stays no more than one day the field still may be used for 3 or 4 years, but after that time the reindeer must stay away for 5 to 6 years until the lichens can grow back. If they graze heavily, say for a few days in one area, they may have to wait 20 years before the lichens grow back. It is not just the eating of the plants, but also the trampling of thousands of sharp hooves that destroys them. In the wintertime the trampling may turn the snow to ice, which smothers and kills these delicate lichens.

It is easy to understand why the reindeer people are nomadic. They must keep the herds moving, and fast. Their very lives depend upon living within the unwritten rules of the ecosystem.

The reindeer people use only the reindeer meat for nourishment. Reindeer milk is occasionally drunk as a rare treat but most doe milk must be saved for the fawns.

Since a small family must have a minimum of 30 reindeer to eat during the year in order to survive, they must keep a herd of at least 100 deer. And if a family owns only 100, they are still living dangerously. Any extremely bad weather, disease, or other catastrophe is liable to mean starvation. A change in some other link of the ecosystem can also bring disaster. One time, for example, there was a measles epidemic among the children of the Chukchi in northeastern Siberia. Many herds were scattered and lost forever because the children were the ones responsible for keeping the reindeer together.

Reindeer people moving off from camp

Agriculture is only possible within the valleys. Even there, it is limited to a very few, hardy vegetables and grains—such as beets, radishes, oats, and barley—that can grow in poor soil and reach maturity during the short growing season. Hay can be grown in the valleys for use by horses and cattle, and it is expected these animals will be more common in the future in the small pastures on river islands or terraces along the rivers.

In the agricultural experiment station at Yakutsk everyone has great hopes for hot-house agriculture. Gas has been found outside Yakutsk and there are possibilities for discovering gas in other places within the taiga, which would provide the necessary heat for large scale hot-house agriculture.

The cost of bringing in and laying gas pipelines would be extremely high for this wild part of the world, but one man has had a wonderful thought that may solve this problem. He believes they could bore tunnels through the rock-hard permafrost and let gas run through them just as though they were metal pipes.

If this idea works and inexpensive gas is piped into the taiga, all kinds of things may happen. New mines could be opened to take out new resources because food for miners would be available from the hothouses of the nearest town. Mines could be heated, miners' homes could be heated and life made more bearable. If there were thus more human activity in the area, there would be a need for roads, airports, river boats, docks, gasoline storage, and so forth. All these changes throughout the ecosystem would have been caused by an idea in the mind of one small unit, a man.

WATER

Food is certainly an absolute necessity for man's continued survival, but equally crucial is a supply of drinking water. During the summer months there is usually enough water in the streams, but wells cannot be used in this region because the soil is frozen and will not release its water content the way regular, unfrozen soil does. It is very difficult for a town or little village to pipe water to outlying cabins. The water will freeze in the pipes almost every month of the year. It is possible to heat the pipes with electric wires or steam, as they do at military installations in Siberia, but a small village cannot afford such luxury.

Most people in the taiga have to live along the rivers in order to have water. In the summer it is simply a matter of hauling buckets of water up from the river. Getting water during the winter is another story. If the river does not freeze to the bottom, the children, who are always the water carriers, continue to haul buckets even though the air temperature drops to 60 degrees below zero. If the river does freeze solid, as all but the largest do, the children must cut and haul snow or ice to melt for drinking water. It takes about 10 buckets of snow to melt down to 1 bucket of water. People here learn, as do those in a dry desert, to make one bucket of water stretch a long way. Water in winter is a valuable resource and is treated as such.

The camps of reindeer people follow river valleys whenever possible. They do this partly because it is generally easier moving and partly because there is fuel within the woods which are generally thicker near the rivers. This is particularly true as the rivers leave the true taiga and flow out into the tundra where trees are extremely valuable resources. The camps also follow the rivers for the easy water supply.

Next to having enough food and water in this wild environment is the requirement to keep from actually freezing to death. These people may not complain about the deep cold as much as a stranger to the area might, but they do feel it and know its dangers. There are three main parts to the problem of keeping warm. There is first the need for special clothing; second, the need for shelter from the weather; and third, the need for fuel to warm the shelter.

CLOTHING

The people of Siberia, especially the native people, have adapted to their environment by wearing animal skins and furs. They may trade at some city like Verkhoyansk for some woolen or cotton clothing, but these are mostly for summer wear. It is almost impossible to find anything better for the deep winter than the reindeer skin and fur. The amazing thing about this skin is that it stays soft and flexible even at temperatures more than 100 degrees below freezing. Other materials or skins of non-Arctic animals become brittle and hard at such temperatures. An ordinary leather jacket would feel like a piece of armor—and bend about as well.

The reindeer people wear at least two layers of fur clothing. The inner layer has the hair facing in toward the body to trap some of the body heat. The other layer faces outward for two reasons. The hair acts as a wind-break in the same way that a forest slows a wind down to almost nothing. This outward-facing fur also traps some escaping body heat. The skins let some heat and perspiration out through their pores, keeping the man from becoming soaking wet inside. In winter everyone wears fur coats, fur pants, fur boots, fur hats, and fur gloves. There is no other way to survive.

Reindeer people must wear clothes of animal skins and furs in order to survive the severe winter cold

SHELTER

The fur clothing serves well while people are moving and making their own internal heat, but when they stop work for the day there must be something additional to keep out the cold. For this reason the people of the reindeer also use animal skins for shelters. They build tents very much like the American Indians' tepee, but made of reindeer, or occasionally moose, hides.

In the winter, when the reindeer camps have retreated back into the taiga, the men cut new poles every day to support the tepee skins. In the summer, however, when they migrate north into the tundra where trees are scarce, they carry tepee poles with them. They are not easy to carry, since every tepee must have more than a dozen poles, each of which measures 12 to 15 feet long. They are stacked on long sleds pulled by trained reindeer. The remaining sleds are loaded with tepee skins, food, and other possessions. A camp herding several thousand reindeer may involve 8 or 10 families, perhaps 30 people. When all their tepees are pulled down every morning and piled on sleds there is quite a caravan setting off into the bleak terrain.

Not everyone in the taiga lives in reindeer skin tepees, just these nomadic tribes of reindeer herders. There are many other people who live in different kinds of shelters. Verkhoyansk, the largest town in the Yana analog region, has mostly log buildings. There are two main reasons for this. First, the town is located within the taiga forest where logs are readily obtained. Second, thick logs provide better insulation, compared to ordinary boards, so they are neces-

Reindeer skins are used for tents by nomadic herders

sary in this frigid land. The logs are not enough insulation, however, and people with any money at all will plaster their log houses on the outside as well as on the inside.

These settlement people also use another naturally available resource of excellent insulation, the reindeer lichen. Evidence of its high insulation value can be seen in the forest where a few inches of lichens will keep permafrost in the soil from melting well into August. Soil nearby, without lichens, will be thawed down to a depth of several feet by August. The people of Verkhoyansk lay a deep layer of these lichens above their ceilings, below the floor, and within their walls to keep the heat in and the cold out.

FUEL

The Russians who move in to run the local government often construct regular buildings such as those in Moscow, but tremendous amounts of fuel are required to keep them as warm as a well-made log/plaster/lichen cabin. Although there are large reserves of coal in Siberia, it is not yet easily or inexpensively come by. Wood has always been, and continues to be, the primary fuel of the taiga.

Wood is burned by the nomadic herders and its availability actually determines to some extent the routes these people will follow. The day's trek must end at a point where wood is close at hand. The settlement people burn wood in their stoves and many men make their living cutting and delivering it to the families in the towns, particularly the larger towns like Verkhoyansk. Families cut and haul their own supplies in the tiny villages and small groups of cabins along the rivers of the taiga.

The people living near the few existing coal mines are able to afford coal for their stoves. Gas and oil production is very small across the taiga, so very little is used for fuel. The Siberians are tying many dreams of a better future to the possibility that gas may become easily available for home fuel throughout much of the taiga. This may be many years away, but they are all very hopeful. The new gas fields northwest of Yakutsk, not too far from the Yana analog area, may someday provide fuel for places like Verkhoyansk, and certainly for Yakutsk, a city of 90,000 people.

COMMUNICATION

In addition to the rather simple but crucial ecosystem links of food, water, clothing, shelter, and fuel, there are links of greater complexity further up the ladder of civilization. For example, man seems to find that communication links with others of his kind extremely important. Perhaps lower forms of life consider it equally important, but man certainly puts much more of his total effort into the business of communicating.

In many societies there is an entire industry called "communications." Among other things it includes the telephone, radio, television, newspapers, magazines, and books. Even the production and emplacement of instructional signs along highways and within buildings is a part of a larger communication system.

It is quite easy to imagine that even a temporary stopping of communications in a city could cause complete chaos. But what would be the effects in the Siberian taiga?

As long as the reindeer people can still use their voices as a means of communication their lives will hardly be affected at all. Even if all mechanical or electronic communication systems in the entire world were stopped some day, the people of the reindeer might never know it had happened. After all, why should they care? No bright green signs tell the children of the reindeer people where to herd the beasts for better grass or lichens. No green light tells them when they can drive 300 animals across a roaring stream. They do not depend upon a bunch of dancers on a television screen to entertain them around the campfire. If they want to see a dance, they jump up and do it. These people do not observe action, they act. They do not get the news about where the mosquitoes are bad or the wood supply good from their morning newspaper or radio. They do, however, have their own unique communication system.

Sometimes news of importance is told to them by hunters. These are often single men who do not want to or are unable to be owners or managers of large herds. They move around alone through the taiga hunting meat for themselves and furs to trade for other things of value. They know they can always get a free meal at any of the camps by giving news, or gossip, about the last camps they dropped in on.

In any society there are the misfits, those who are mentally or physically weak. In advanced societies these people have very little value, but in the nomadic reindeer-people society they become communicators. They drift from camp

Reindeer racing is a popular sport at fairs

to camp looking for hand-outs from relatives, friends, or helpful strangers, and as they move about they pick up information and transmit it far and wide. One wonders about how true some of their information may be, but they probably pass on valuable news about such things as animal pasturage possibilities, diseases of animals or people at different camps, good watering places, and upcoming fairs and festivals.

Fairs and festivals are communication links in themselves. People come many miles to these fairs where trading is done, games are played, and information exchanged. Sometimes an important camp leader will be invited to a fair by a personal messenger. This messenger is also a communication link and he travels faster than you might imagine. One Chukchi messenger won a foot race at a fair and is reported to have run all the way to his home camp with the great news—a distance of 500 miles.

Lamut natives have been reported to be able to run fast enough to overtake a reindeer fleeing for its life. They have been seen chasing and keeping up with reindeer even while running behind a dog team and sled.

Yakut women come to a fair in their native costumes

TRANSPORTATION

Most communication cannot take place without some form of transportation. Sometimes, in fact, there is no difference between them. If a piece of information is moved through a telephone wire (transportation) and is received by a listener (communication), what is a telephone system? Is it a transportation system or a communication system? If a man is driving to New York City in the morning (transportation) to talk with a banker about borrowing money (communication) what is the highway system? Is it a transportation system or simply an important communication link between one brain and another?

It is clear in Siberia, though, that a dog sled loaded with tent poles is acting as a transportation system. In much of the taiga, particularly the southern parts, dogs and sleds provide most of the transportation, other than that provided by human legs. The northern parts of the taiga and the tundra see the use of more reindeer sleds than dog sleds.

Verkhoyansk and Yakutsk are served today by modern aircraft. The taiga of Canada and Alaska is famous for its bush pilots who fly in and out of remote areas. They not only provide transportation but also bring news of all kinds to the people of the north country, just as the wandering hunters do for the nomadic reindeer people of Siberia.

The rivers of the World Taiga are, and have always been, an extremely important element of the transportation link of the taiga ecosystem. Most villages of the far north are along major rivers; partly for their use as water transporta-

A steamship sails up the Lena River

tion routes, and partly for their use as a source of water and fish.

Yakutsk is served by large river steamers on the Lena River from the Arctic Ocean sea lanes to the north and other cities to the south. Some of these freight-carrying ships are luxurious and carry perhaps 100 people up and down the Lena on business or pleasure. They can only operate about four months of the year when the ice is gone and the water level is adequately high. The frozen rivers are the winter highways for dog teams, reindeer sleds, and people on foot, skis, or snowshoes. Rivers, the taiga forest, and reindeer seem to provide all the necessities of life for these hardy people.

SOCIETY AND GOVERNMENT

People, as small family groups, do not lead very complex lives. The relationships between them are simple and their needs are not too much different from those of an individual or two. When their numbers grow, however, there develops a need for cooperation among the individuals to assure their continued survival and to keep life as pleasant as possible.

Groups of people so dependent upon their natural environment find themselves in trouble unless they develop certain understandings, certain rules, certain agreements about who will pasture his reindeer where; who will cut wood where; and who will get his water from which pool. Without these agreements they would find their pastures ruined, the limited woods of the far northern pastures deforested, and several pools dried up. When rules and regulations get very complex and special people are named to invent and enforce them we call it a *government*. At first, while the rules are simple and probably not even written down, the people are informally governed by their *society*. There are perhaps no formal rules or over-all rulers, but people know from family training and from watching others just what it is that one ought or ought not do.

Religious ideas overlap so completely into society and the beginnings of government that it is often impossible to decide which is a society or government rule and which is a religious one. Certain religious and society rules in the communities along the Yana also turn out to serve as "natural laws" that help the people and their herds survive in a difficult environment.

The reindeer people along the Yana do not think of themselves as operating in the form of tribes or in the form of a state, or county, or family, as most peoples do, but instead as a series of *camps*. A reindeer camp may be just one family and its animals, but it is more apt to be made up of several families and their combined herds.

The entire social structure is built around the herd. The people, their animals, and their feeding ranges are a simple, but excellent example of an ecosystem at work. Every element in the system is affected by every other element.

The size of the herd determines the general well-being of a family. It takes about 100 animals to keep a small family alive and healthy. If the number drops much lower there is some question as to whether the family can survive alone. They may be forced to join another camp and become workers for the strong man of that camp. While a herd of 100 may be the smallest, some camps have a herd of 3,000 to 5,000 reindeer. The herds cannot be allowed to grow much larger or the ecosystem gets out of balance.

There are certain parts of the surrounding ecosystem, the natural environment, which are at work to keep the herd sizes from growing too much. There are *severe weather conditions* that kill animals directly or indirectly by first killing plants, which then causes starvation among the reindeer. Unusually warm summers allow a hoof disease to become epidemic and kill off thousands of reindeer.

Because mosquitoes and flies bother the reindeer and sometimes stampede them into herds of their wild brothers in the taiga, the men often build large, smoky fires to drive away the insects. This works fairly well except that the *fires kill the lichens and mosses* upon which the reindeer depend. If these fires are not put out they may spread as smoky, non-flaming, underground fires and continue to smolder for years. Another, rather unpleasant, force at work keeping the herd size down to a balanced ecosystem level, is that of *death within the human population.* If a disease strikes the people of the camp and kills some of them, the entire system is disrupted. Since there are then fewer people to round up the herd and keep it moving out, the animals tend to drift off into the wild herds.

Keeping enough animals in a herd to allow for the fact that something unexpected may happen—and yet keeping the herd size down below the size where it begins to work against its own survival possibilities, is a continual battle. Although natural forces are at work to maintain the ecosystem balance, human society has also developed, over the centuries, customs and rules that enable them to do two opposite things at the same time: increase the size of their small herds to assure survival of the humans; and decrease the size of the large herds, for the same purpose. The end result of these two opposite forces should be a balanced ecosystem in which animal, plant, and man can survive.

A poor man finds it difficult to increase the size of his herd very rapidly by himself, so he may join with another poor man and his herd. A larger herd also helps enlarge itself because wild reindeer are more easily attracted to join it. A large herd also means the breeding of more animals and the large numbers can help fight off attacks by wolves, wolverines, and bears. Sometimes the joining together is a temporary agreement between two head men, and it may be broken off later on.

If a man can find no one to join with, he may resort to stealing in order to keep his herd up to the number necessary to feed his family. If he is a violent man he will drive his small herd right into the middle of a rich man's much larger herd. As they disentangle the herds he will take away some of the rich man's young deer that have not yet been branded, or marked. This leads to many long arguments, fights, and occasional killing. The rich camp leader will often let the poor man get away with it rather than take the risk of getting himself or his herders killed. He knows that a shortage of men in his camp would unbalance his ecosystem.

A young man with no herd or too small a herd may sign up with a rich man and act as his assistant for a period of years. The young assistant and his family are fed and clothed by the rich man as though part of his family. He is paid every year in does. He might receive anywhere from 5 to 10 does per year so that after 10 or 15 years of assistantship he can leave and take a herd large enough to support him and his family. Meanwhile, he has learned all the wisdom and tricks-of-the-trade from the strong man.

Some men decide to get a herd the easy way, by marrying the strong man's daughter. Often, however, it turns out not to be an easy route to riches after all. The future father-in-law wants to be certain that the future son-in-law will be able to take good care of his daughter, so he puts the young man through a period of several years of intensive, hard work and harsh abuse. If he proves to be a strong, willing worker, and a good herdsman, the marriage will be approved. The new bride will be given a small personal herd to take with her and the son-in-law is given "freedom of one day." This means that he can keep as many of the strong man's animals as he can run down and brand with his mark on this one day.

The man at the highest end of the social scale is the one with a large herd of thousands of deer. Although nature is at work keeping his herd size down by various catastrophes, society must also exercise some controls in order to keep the size of the herd in balance with the ecosystem. It is absolutely necessary that some kind of control exist because the reindeer reproduce quite well.

A herd of reindeer being run down for branding

The does are ready to give birth to a fawn in the spring after the spring of their own birth. They will give birth (calve) every spring for the following 12 to 15 years. Just to demonstrate how rapidly the numbers go up on this basis—if the herd had 1,000 does at the beginning of this year, there would be 51,000 does ready for breeding within only 15 springs. Such reproduction, without the controls that have developed, would completely upset the balance.

Herds are divided up in several ways, each of which helps the ecosystem. We have just mentioned the system of assistantship. Any very large camp will have some number of assistants who are ready to set off on their own with the herd they have earned over the years.

Men who have finished their long courtship rites with their fathers-in-law divide the large herd up by taking their new wives' private herds and the ones they managed to mark through the "freedom of one day" plan.

Men with the very large herds also keep the herd numbers down by sacrificing reindeer for many different reasons. The men probably do not realize that they are killing the animals to balance the ecosystem. The sacrifices are now simply part of their religion and custom. When everyone comes back to winter quarters after a summer of nomadic wandering there is a great celebration for which many animals are killed and eaten.

The sacrificed animals provide not only meat and milk for the festival, but badly needed skins for clothing and for trading. Animals are also slaughtered at the winter solstice, the longest night of the year. This seems a very important date when you live right on the Arctic Circle because this is the one and only day of the year when the sun does not rise.

Custom also allows the people of the reindeer to sacrifice animals at the beginning of a big trip, the return from a big trip, or when the moon is new. Two days after someone dies it is the custom that the family of that person prepare food and take it to any camps within 50 miles. Each and every guest at the funeral is given a reindeer.

It should be clear now that social, religious, and traditional customs have developed over the centuries to help keep down the size of the largest herds. These manmade actions are combined with other natural forces to keep the best possible balance for the survival of the ecosystem.

The reindeer people along the Yana live under the governmental rule of the Union of Soviet Socialist Republics. They live in the largest of the 15 Soviet Socialist Republics, the Russian Soviet Federated Socialist Republic.

Their large Republic happens also to be made up of 15 other units of government called Autonomous Republics. The Yana River area falls within the largest of these, Yakut, or as it would appear on official maps—Yakut Autonomous Soviet Socialist Republic, or Yakut A.S.S.R. But, as was mentioned earlier, most of the people in the far north are governed more by the laws of nature, religion, and social customs than by a government many thousands of miles away in Moscow.

COMMERCE AND INDUSTRY

Further up the ecosystem ladder are links that are less important in terms of survival. After a people has satisfied

Trees cut in the taiga forests are carried to sawmills

their needs for food and water they look for ways to satisfy their needs for clothing, shelter, and fuel. Each link is a so-called higher order of civilization.

People living in highly civilized societies hardly have to worry about satisfying the lower ecosystem needs and instead seem to spend most of their energies at commerce and industry. Along the Yana, however, there is relatively little commerce or industry.

There is one industry that is fairly active within the forests of the taiga. About one-half of the forest resources of the Soviet Union lie in the taiga, particularly in eastern Siberia. About one-sixth of the sawn lumber in the Soviet Union comes from eastern Siberia and the Far East. There are sawmills in almost every town in Siberia and particularly along the Trans-Siberian Railroad. Most of the small villages along the northward flowing rivers are sawmill towns. The lumber is floated north to be carried on larger ships through the Northern Sea Route to foreign markets. The town of Igarka on the Yenisei River is one important lumbering, sawmilling, and woodworking point. Farther down the Yenisei is the city of Norilsk, which owes its growth to copper and nickel mining and smelting. It now has a population of some 110,000, which makes it the 136th largest city in the Soviet Union, in spite of its location at 69°20′ N latitude. It is much further north than Fairbanks, Alaska, and yet more than four times larger in population. It is a rarity in the far north, but perhaps it is a sample of what may come as transportation improves and as the Soviet Union's easily obtained mineral supplies deplete and it must turn to the taiga.

Yakutsk, capital of Yakut A.S.S.R., is the most commercially active city in the area near the Yana River region. It is a port on the important Lena River and is on a highway leading south to the Trans-Siberian Railroad. It is most noted for its sawmills, shipyards, coal mines, wood products, shoe and clothing manufacturing. Its rapidly increasing population of about 90,000 is busy carrying out the above activities, running the Republic's government and various research laboratories concerned with the problems of life in the far north.

Although there are these few fairly active cities within the taiga, the area in general is one of wilderness with little commerce or industry.

WORLD AREAS OF TUNDRA
ATLANTIC
OCEAN
NEWFOUNDLAND
50°
60°
NORTH SEA
ICELAND
ARCTIC CIRCLE
66⅔°
70°
Bergen
NORWAY
SWEDEN
FINLAND
Archangel
GREENLAND
BAFFIN ISLAND
DAVIS STRAIT
HUDSON BAY
Fort Churchill
Churchill River
CANADA
TUNDRA
ELLESMERE ISLAND
SPITZBERGEN ISLANDS
0°
NORTH POLE
FRANZ JOSEF LAND
ARCTIC
OCEAN
NOVAYA ZEMLYA
YUKON TERRITORY
Junea
Yukon River
Fort Yukon
ARCTIC SLOPE
Barrow
Fairbanks
Nenana
Anchorage
ALASKA
TUNDRA ANALOG AREA
CHUKCHI SEA
Kivalina
Kotzebue
Nome
WRANGEL ISLAND
90°
OSTROV OKTYABARSKOY REVOLYUTSII
Ob River
Dudinka
Norilsk
Igarka
Yenisei River
LAPTEV SEA
NEW SIBERIAN ISLANDS
CHUKCHI PENINSULA
TUNDRA
SOVIET UNION
Lena River
TAIGA ANALOG AREA
Verkhoyansk
VERKHOYANSKI KHREBET
CHERSKI KHREBET
ARCTIC CIRCLE
66⅔°
60°
BERING SEA
Yakutsk
Magadan
KAMCHATKA
LAKE BAIKAL
SEA OF OKHOTSK
SAKHALINE ISLAND
TUNDRA ANALOG AREA
CHUKCHI SEA
Point Hope
Kivalina R.
Kivalina
Wulik River
Noatak
Noatak River
Kotzebue

TUNDRA

There is another vast area of the world above the Arctic Circle which, although still called "Arctic," is very different from the taiga type of Arctic environment. The terrain looks different, the vegetation is vastly different, and the people of the tundra have had to adopt different methods for surviving in this harsh world.

LOCATION

The tundra region of the Arctic is a cold, treeless area generally to the north of the taiga. Between the taiga of Siberia and the Arctic Ocean are hundreds of thousands of square miles of what some have called "the barren lands." Great expanses of Canada and Alaska also fall under the classification of tundra.

The analog area chosen to represent the tundra is in northwestern Alaska on the coast of the Chukchi Sea, a part of the Arctic Ocean. The circular analog area is set directly on the Arctic Circle with the 164° 30′ W longitude line running through the center. The ecosystem of the tundra is so much affected by the sea that a large portion has been included in the circle. Most tundra people around the world are like the people in the village of Kivalina (Kiv-a-leena), Alaska, in that they live primarily from the resources of the sea.

CLIMATE

Temperatures along the coast of the Chukchi are far different from those at inland Verkhoyansk or even inland Fairbanks, Alaska. During Kivalina's summer months the normal high temperature recorded here is around 55° F. The highest temperature recorded here was 72° F in July 1956.

In mid-winter the temperature around Kivalina drops to an average of 10° F to 15° F below zero. The lowest temperature ever recorded in Kivalina was 48° below zero, whereas at Verkhoyansk it frequently drops from the normal of 57° below to 70° and 80° below, with an all-time low of –89° F.

The amount of precipitation at Kivalina is also different from that of the taiga. The northwestern stretch of Alaska's coast can expect from 10 to 15 inches of rain each year, about five times as much as falls at Verkhoyansk. About half of the total arrives during August and September. One might expect that even more rain would fall on an area so close to the sea, but even the summer air is too cold to carry much moisture. The Chukchi is frozen almost solid for many months, so the air cannot draw much moisture from the sea during the winter either.

Precipitation of snow in the winter is also quite different from the taiga country. It is not unusual for this region in Alaska to have a total snowfall of 40 inches, with perhaps half that amount on the ground at any one time. The typical taiga near Verkhoyansk has a total fall of perhaps 5 inches.

Another great difference in the climate of these two types of "Arctic" is the number of clear-sky days. Winter days in the taiga are mostly clear with no clouds. Kivalina's winter days are usually cloudy, with at least half the blue sky hidden. Kivalina's summer days are even worse, with only about a quarter of the blue sky showing on an average day.

This part of Alaska is noted for its high winter winds, another contrast to the taiga's complete calm during the deep cold of winter. Kivalina has an average winter wind speed of 15 miles per hour. A wind like that, combined with a temperature 5° or 10° below zero, produces much worse living conditions than does Siberia with temperatures of

A dog sled out in the windswept wilderness

–70° with no wind. Young people driving dog teams in such winds have been lost for hours and sometimes days. The drifting snow soon hides the trails even though they may be marked by sticks or old oil drums. It is the dogs that eventually lead them home, since they can follow scents and sounds from a village several miles away.

MOUNTAINS AND MINERALS

Too often people get the impression that the tundra is a flat plain. It is flat in many parts of the world but by no means everywhere. In the Canadian mainland the tundra is rather flat, but not without some rolling hills of rock. The islands of the Canadian tundra, however, are extremely mountainous, as are the Soviet islands. The tundra of Norway is primarily in the central mountains, and much of Alaska's tundra lands are in mountainous areas. The northwestern coast of Alaska around Kivalina is neither a vast rolling plain nor towering mountains, but low mountains, rolling hills, and level sections.

The analog area around Kivalina is situated in the arctic foothills, west of the famous Brooks Range of mountains that lies across the top of Alaska. The DeLong Mountains, part of the Brooks Range, provide the highest elevations in the area, about 3,000 feet higher than the sea-level village of Kivalina. The Baird Mountains to the south of the DeLong Mountains are also quite high, with occasional peaks as tall as 4,600 feet.

There are two level sections within the analog area. Three or four miles of land around Kivalina are very flat, cut only

The Baird Mountains south of the Brooks Range

by the Kivalina and Wulik Rivers as they flow from the DeLongs to the sea. There is another small, flat section along the Noatak River which runs west between the De-Longs and Bairds, past the Eskimo village of Noatak, and out into the sea across the sound from the "city" of Kotze-bue (coats-eh-boo).

Although the Arctic foothills may be shown in the future to contain valuable resources, they are not noted today for their mineral possibilities. In the Kivalina area the hills and mountains are made primarily of mudstones, sandstones, limestones, and flint. Most of the rock is covered by only 5 to 10 feet of sands, gravels, and soils of various types.

Oil and gas deposits have not been discovered in the Kivalina area, but the tundra north of the Brooks Range, called the Arctic Slope, has been producing oil for many years. The Canadian Arctic islands are being explored today and show great promise of oil and gas production.

An unusual exception to the general lack of resources in the Arctic foothills are the mineral deposits on the tundra around Nome, Alaska. Here there are placer (plass-er) deposits of heavy minerals such as tin, platinum, and gold in the sands and gravels of the tundra coastal plain. Heavy minerals are deposited by flooding streams that come out of the mineralized mountains of the interior during the spring. They are dropped in the same general section of the stream beds where the streams slow down and lose their ability to carry such heavy minerals. Men came from all over the world in the 1800's to work the gold placers of Nome after they had tried for their fortunes in the placers of Fairbanks, and earlier, in the placers of the Yukon Territory in Canada.

SOILS AND PERMAFROST

One element of the natural environment that is much the same in the tundra as in the taiga is permafrost. The tundra is the real land of permafrost and it dominates everything about the soil of the area. Scientists have drilled holes around Kivalina and found permanently frozen soil and rock all the way down to 1,165 feet.

Frost-distorted terrain of the tundra

As in the taiga, a prominent natural feature caused by the permafrost is the pingo. There are only a few pingoes spread over the Kivalina area, but there are many other patterned ground formations caused by the interaction between soil and ice. These other formations are much smaller in size, but much more numerous.

A walk across the tundra in the spring is full of surprises. Where the soil was forced up by the fall freezing and where some of it has dropped back down during the thaw, there are often hollow humps. These humps look solid, until someone steps on them. They collapse because there is nothing inside. This would not be so bad if one could count on it. The next little bump, however, turns out to be solid as a rock. This bump has a center of solid ice that will melt during the summer, but is now protected from the warming sun by a layer of lichens.

There are large areas of the tundra where stones are arranged in very definite geometric patterns that geographers call *patterned ground.* Often there are patterns of stone circles that touch each other and form an entire field of stone rings. The center of each circle is made mostly of clay and other small-grained soils and supports no vegetation at all. The rocky areas, like little stone walls separating these small, circular fields, will usually have some grasses and lichens growing among the rocks. These "edge" areas can grow vegetation because they are not areas of churning. The muddy centers, however, are zones of mixing and churning. Any plant seeds dropped there are soon mixed down too deep into the mud to sprout.

Scientists do not know exactly what goes on in these circles, but apparently the "centers of action" somehow start churning and keep forcing large stones to the surface. The same action gradually, over the years, slides these stones along the surface of the ground out away from the center. After awhile, the stones moving out from one center bump into those moving out from other centers and can move no further. Sometimes the patterns have a number of straight sides, often five or six, and are called soil polygons.

VEGETATION

The various forms of patterned ground make the terrain of the tundra unique in appearance, but the characteristic most noticeable to people from other areas is the total absence of trees. There are some, of course, at the southern edge where the tundra meets the taiga, but out on the true tundra there is nothing that would qualify as a tree. There is the occasional willow or alder bush, but scientists do not classify these as trees.

There are a number of factors acting together to keep trees from living on the tundra. Strangely enough, there is a winter drought that limits the growth of trees. During these long months there is little unfrozen moisture available to trees. The dry winter winds blowing across the tundra quickly evaporate any moisture that does become available. Some Arctic plants avoid this drying action of the wind by dying down in the winter and surviving underground as roots that send up new sprouts in the spring and summer.

The short growing season also prevents the growth of trees and limits the types of plants that can survive on the open tundra. There is apt to be frost in the air every month of the year, which tends to keep plants from even getting started.

The village of Kivalina lies about 100 miles north of the "tree line" and about 50 miles north of the alder brush country. All plants in the area are very low, the tallest on dry soil being only several inches high. Plants growing on the edges of ponds tend to grow several feet high, but the overall impression a man gets upon looking around is that there is nothing taller than his moccasin.

There are many plant species present in the area, including cotton grass which grows in wet areas and has a fluffy, white flower that resembles a cotton boll. There are green and yellow sphagnum (sfagg-numb) mosses that absorb water like a sponge. They do not look particularly wet, but water gushes out if someone steps on them. Lichens are everywhere. There are over 80 different species of lichen for caribou (a North American relative of the reindeer) to eat in the Kivalina area.

There are Labrador tea plants, bright yellow buttercups, sedges, foxtail, timothy and fescue grasses, all of which are familiar to those living in the middle latitudes and high altitudes around the world. In addition, there are known to be over 300 species of tiny plants within the area. The land is barren compared with many other places in the world, but it is certainly not completely bare.

RIVERS

The rivers of the Kivalina area, and in those parts of the World Tundra not far from the sea, are not quite so important as the rivers in the taiga, but they are still not to be ignored. The sea itself takes over some of a river's importance in transportation, communication, food, and water.

The most important rivers around Kivalina are the Kivalina, the Wulik, and the Noatak. The 360-mile-long Noatak, which begins high in the Brooks Range, is the only river in the region that does not hibernate by freezing solid during the winter. It has thick ice, of course, but there is always water running below. The Kivalina River provides drinking water for the people in Kivalina, 6 miles away.

The Noatak River is different in that it runs through

wooded country. This is the last of the trees. Beyond the Noatak the trees fail to grow, so that by the latitude of Kivalina, which is but 40 or 50 miles further north, there are no trees at all. As a boat proceeds upstream from the delta, in water with very strong rapids, it passes below cliffs and through increasingly wooded country. Eskimo history reports that people used to live in these woods (the edge of the taiga) and were called *Naupatarmiut*, or "the people of the woods." The Eskimos who now live along the river and who use boats to travel and hunt are known as *Noatagmiut*, "river people." The river at the little village of Noatak is about 900 feet wide, and 50 log cabins and huts are set high up on top of its muddy, black banks. The banks are covered with brush and the hillsides are green with spruce.

The Wulik and Kivalina Rivers both enter the sea through the Kivalina Lagoon. Along much of the tundra in Alaska the rivers enter lagoons like the one at Kivalina. These shallow lakes are formed by long sand bars on their seaward sides. These bars are thrown up by storm waves and keep the fresh water of the rivers from emptying directly into the sea. The fresh water of the lagoon gradually seeps away to the sea through the sands of the bars. In the spring when the rivers are aflood and pouring vast quantities of fresh water into the lagoons, these shallow lakes fill up and break through the sand bars, as though breaking dams, and rush into the sea. Later, the natural dams are repaired by the ocean as new storms occur and as sea ice bulldozes the bottom and piles it up on the bars.

These fresh-water bodies are extremely important to the people of Kivalina. Because they are not very salty, the ice that forms on the lagoons is excellent for winter drinking water when the rivers run dry. The Kivalina and Wulik Rivers hibernate during most winters and provide no fresh running water. Most of the World Tundra contains an enormous number of ponds and lakes. The Kivalina area is an exception and has very few ponds because solid rock is but a few inches down and because the area is too hilly.

PONDS AND LAKES

Although there are few ponds around the Kivalina portion of the tundra, the Arctic Slope of Alaska has more ponds and lakes than anyone could imagine. The same is true along the western shores of Hudson Bay in Canada and along the Arctic coast of Siberia. When anyone tries to get across this kind of country in the summer he will agree that in many regions the tundra is a million bodies of water separated from each other by soggy ground.

The lakes are usually quite shallow, anywhere from a few inches to about 6 or 8 feet at most. The terrain is so level that the lakes find it difficult to empty themselves by rivers and creeks, the way most lakes do. In other flat places of the world, lakes lose their water by leakage down into the ground. These millions of Arctic ponds cannot get rid of their water that way, however, because the frozen ground below will not allow seepage. These tundra ponds, swamps, bogs, and lakes just sit there and breed mosquitoes, tabanids, and black flies. Children of the tundra swim in these shallow lakes which warm up to a terribly cold temperature in August. It is so much fun that the children ignore their private clouds of biting flies that patiently wait out each ducking and bobbing of their host's head.

One interesting fact about the lakes on the Arctic Slope of Alaska is that many thousands of them are rectangular. Their long direction is a little bit west of north, and all the lakes are lined up this way. Scientists still do not know why these lakes came to be rectangular or why they all face the same direction.

ANIMALS

A land of such cold, such winds, and so little vegetation hardly seems likely to have many animals living on it. It does not really have very many different species, but some of them are great in numbers. Scientists have found only about 25 different species of mammals, 13 of which are very important to man. These are marked by an asterisk.

Land Animals

*Caribou
Moose
*Arctic Shrew
*Arctic Fox
Weasel
Hoary Marmot
*Alaska Vole
*Collared Lemming
River Otter

*Polar Bear
*Masked Shrew
*Red Fox
Wolverine
Red-backed Vole
Muskrat
Porcupine
Lynx

*Grizzly Bear
*Wolf
Ermine
*Ground Squirrel
*Tundra Vole
*Brown Lemming
Coyote
Mink

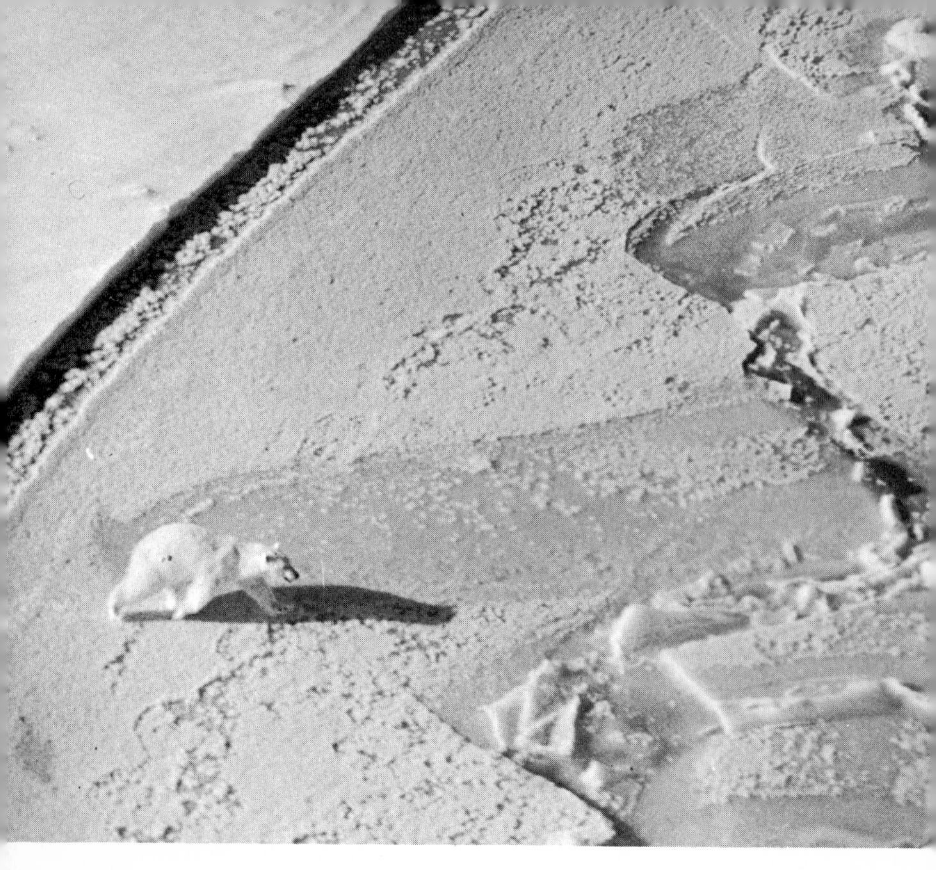

A polar bear on the ice of the Chukchi Sea

Three other species that used to be in the Kivalina area have been killed off completely—white sheep, musk-ox, and the tundra hare. These three species are still found in other parts of the World Tundra, but apparently there has been too much contact with man around Kivalina.

The 25 mammal species, along with the vegetation and marine animals, make up what is called the *food web,* or *food chain,* of the area. Every area of the world has its own food web made up of different animals and plants.

When talking of land animals, everything begins with those animals who eat plants as their most important energy source. These *herbivores* are eaten in turn by the meat-eating *carnivores*. The shrews, voles, lemmings, ground squirrels, and caribou are the main herbivores of the species listed. The carnivores, including man, live by eating these and the other species listed. Unless the various rodents

Moose are often seen in the sparse timber of the Brooks Range

and caribou find enough grasses and lichens to eat, every other species is in extreme danger of starvation and possibly local extinction.

The grizzly bear is fairly common in Kivalina, where he seems to depend a great deal on the Alaska ground squirrels as his main food. He does like to eat berries found in the bushes along stream banks, but he is primarily a carnivore. Frequently he gets meat, not by killing, but by eating caribou meat left by an Eskimo hunter who could not carry it all away. Sometimes the grizzly will eat well by finding the carcass of a sea mammal washed up on a beach. In this way the food web is extended into the usually separate food web of the sea. Scientists working in the area estimate that on any one day there is likely to be one carcass of seal, walrus, or whale for every mile of beach. One carcass of a whale could mean up to 50 tons, or 100,000 pounds, of meat, and this can keep a number of grizzly bears happy—if an animal with the Latin name of *Ursus horribilis* can ever be happy.

The human inhabitants of this region along the coast live mostly on animals taken from the sea, although they do hunt the land animals when there are no marine animals available. They rely on the beluga whale the way people of Siberia rely on the reindeer—that is, they use it for food, fuel, clothing, rope, and many other purposes. The people of Kivalina like caribou skins for certain types of clothing and therefore do hunt on land, but these are coastal people and they love the sea.

The following marine mammals are found in the Chukchi Sea within the Kivalina area.

Sea Animals

Walrus
Spotted Seal
Ribbon Seal
White Whale (beluga)
Pacific Killer Whale
Gray Whale
Sei Whale
Polar Bear
Humpback Whale
Ringed Seal
Bearded Seal
Harbor Porpoise
Finback Whale
Little Piked Whale
Bowhead Whale

Sometimes small herds of walrus stray near Kivalina

A baby spotted seal sunning itself

Although these species are found within the Chukchi Sea, they are not always available to the hunters of Kivalina. Most of the mammals used by Eskimos are not in the Chukchi during the summer months when the sea is free of ice. The hunting of seals and whales must be done from the ice. The best hunting is done during the migration of these animals, both northward in spring and southward in late fall.

The walrus migration route is very far out to sea from Kivalina, but some small herds do occasionally come close enough for Kivalina hunters. The spotted seal is around during the summer, but his meat is not so desirable. His spotted fur, however, is very popular for making fancy boots or slippers for sale to tourists.

The beluga, or white whale, is common in Kivalina and a favorite of the Eskimos for fuel, food, and rope. It is a very small whale, about 10 to 15 feet long and weighing about 1,500 pounds. The great herds migrate north of Kivalina in summer, but a few can be seen all summer long.

White men may not legally hunt the bowhead whale as a business, but the Eskimos may hunt it for their personal use. During the early whaling days of the late 1800's these whales were almost hunted out of existence by the white men. The Eskimos probably kill no more than 30 or 40 throughout the Arctic. This does not cut down the herd size very much, but it does mean as much as 4 million pounds of food, fuel, and other whale parts so valuable to the Eskimo families. One whale means survival over the winter for an entire village.

HUMANS

Apparently the Eskimos migrated from the Orient and this immigration had reached its peak when white men first came in contact with them in about 1740. It is estimated that at that time there were perhaps 100,000 people of Asiatic background living in northwestern North America, about 40,000 of whom were probably of Eskimo stock, more than half of these living in northwest Alaska and in the in-

An Eskimo family hunts walrus from floating ice

Many Eskimo mothers carry their children on their backs

terior. According to early Danish settlers, the Eskimos had spread as far as Greenland by the thirteenth century. The 15,000 Greenland Eskimos have mixed quite thoroughly with the Danes and other non-Eskimos and are now given the respected title of Greenlanders. There are estimated to be about 500 "pure" Eskimos living on the "Barren Lands" of Canada. These are caribou people and, historically, have had little to do with the majority of Eskimos, who are coastal people.

The Eskimos of settlements such as Kivalina, Noatak, Point Hope, and Tigara, retain many of the old ways of survival within the natural environment, but the intrusion of so many white men has caused them also to take on some of their ways.

FOOD

The Eskimos around the Kivalina area buy some food and some materials made by the white man from a little store in Kivalina, Point Hope, Noatak or from a still larger store in Kotzebue. They buy items such as salt, matches, cigarettes, coffee, tea, and candy from the stores, but the really important food for survival still comes from the natural environment—the land, the sea, and the air.

In the Kivalina tundra the *food chain,* which links man (and everyone else) to the natural environment of the ecosystem, is a bit more complicated than the taiga's. The people of the taiga depend almost entirely on the reindeer. There is a very short, uncomplicated food chain from the lichens to the reindeer and directly to man.

Ecologists draw diagrams, or models, to show the ways in which ecosystem units depend on one another. A simple model shows how just a few of the species in the Kivalina area feed on each other. Since food provides necessary energy for all living things, ecologists sometimes call this an *energy flow model.*

The units, such as vegetation, that have the most arrows leaving them are the most essential units in the ecosystem.

The people of Kivalina buy some items in the store

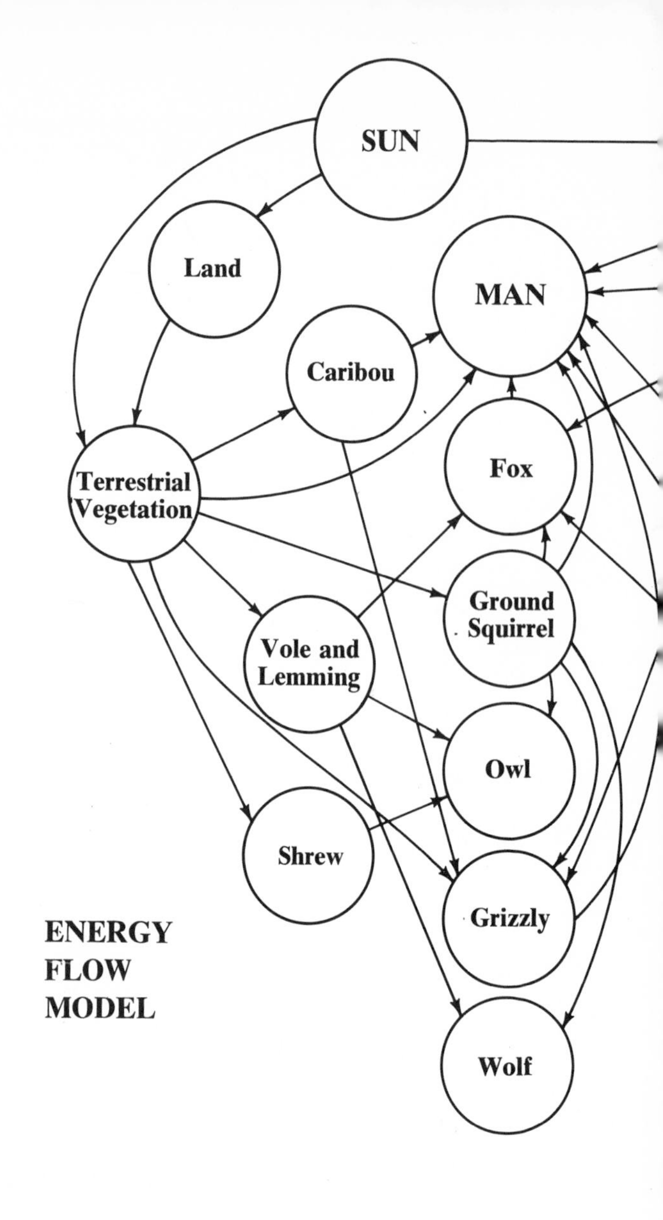

ENERGY FLOW MODEL

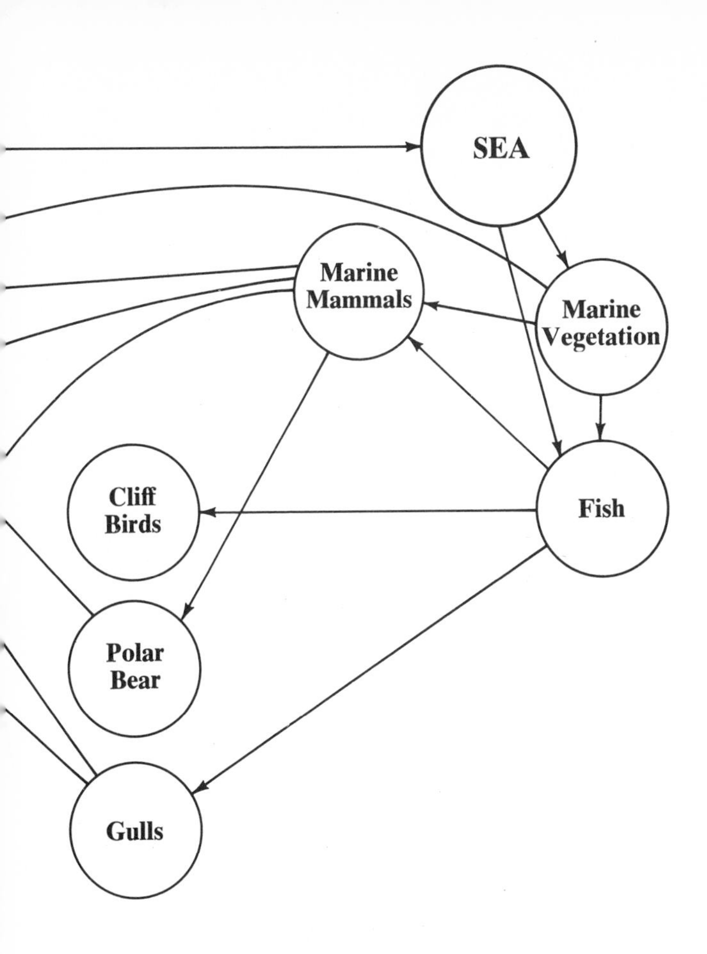

This model shows how very important are the voles, lemmings, and ground squirrels—and how unimportant is man. In other words, if all the ground squirrels suddenly died of some disease, all the animals to which their energy arrows go would begin to starve. If all the men in the area died of some disease, nothing bad would happen to the ecosystem. No energy arrows leave man.

The model includes the marine food chain because the Kivalina area is partly made up of the Chukchi Sea. The Eskimos live on land and sea animals during different seasons. Some animals, like the sea gulls and polar bears, move back and forth between the marine and land chains. Even the grizzly bear and the fox get some of their energy from marine mammals washed up on the shore.

WATER

Although the model does not show it, fresh water is also necessary for survival. Drinking water is not difficult to find during the spring, summer and fall, but supplying drinking water in the winter is a major activity. The Wulik and Kivalina Rivers provide plentiful water for the village of Kivalina, and other rivers are sources for smaller villages within the area. In the winter there is no water in the Wulik, except in the form of ice. The Kivalina River continues to supply water except in very cold winters. The villagers must then get water from the lagoon, which has just enough salt in it to keep from freezing but not so much that it cannot be drunk.

The young people of the village are given the duty of going 6 miles northwest to bring home barrels of water or blocks of ice. They do not object to this duty because it is their rare chance to drive the dog teams on a 12-mile trip over the snow, racing each other on the way out and returning slowly dragging the heavy barrels of water or blocks of ice. When blocks of ice are brought back they are thrown into large oil drums or a large metal can inside the house. A small faucet is plugged into the barrel's side so that melted ice water can be drawn out as needed. In the summer, barrels of fresh water are taken from the mouth of the Wulik, where it enters the lagoon, and are carried by rowboat across the lagoon to the point nearest the village trail. The water is usually left there in large drums for people to draw off with smaller buckets as needed.

When the people are out on the sea ice for days and weeks waiting for whales to migrate past them, they get their drinking water from pools of melted water lying atop the sea ice. Surprisingly, the frozen salt water becomes fresh as it melts.

SHELTER

Eskimos along the Arctic coastlines are most apt to build their homes of wood and sod. Sod blocks are cut from the top few inches of soil, which is mostly roots of existing

A sod hut with whale-rib hitching posts for dog teams

plants, old roots, and semidecayed plant materials, all mixed with sand, silt, and clay. The blocks are laid up like bricks, several blocks deep for insulation, with only an occasional gap left for a window of glass, plastic, or translucent whale intestine. Blocks are piled on the roof, too, leaving a space for a skylight window. The building is at least half underground, with the windows just above ground level. These shelters are reasonably comfortable in the winter when the walls are frozen hard. In the summer warmth they become too damp for comfort, so everyone moves out into tents.

The sod huts are not made of sod alone, they have frames of driftwood or whale bone. The Arctic coastlines are strewn with lumber and tree trunks brought from around the world by unknown ocean currents. The beaches are the only source of building lumber for most people of the tundra. Occasionally a man from Kivalina may work for a summer in Kotzebue, Fairbanks, or Nome and earn enough money to ship in some pieces of plywood from which he will make the best sod hut in town, but lumber is generally too expensive for this use. The only buildings made entirely of wood are those put up by "outsiders," such as a school, a store, a post office, a military building, or a church. Whale and walrus bone may not be as easy to work with, but it is free, lasts far longer than wood, and is a reminder of the past. The teenagers of today do not care for these reminders of their people's primitive past. Most of the young people would rather wear tight blue-jeans and listen to rock-and-roll music than think of their heritage.

Frame houses of Kotzebue

The houses, whether sod or wood, are furnished with an unusual mixture of the primitive and the modern. Their toilet may be an enamel bucket that is emptied into a 55-gallon oil drum that is later hauled out onto the sea ice. When the spring thaw and breakup occur the chunks of ice will carry the drums far out to sea. As the ice melts the drums sink to the bottom.

CLOTHING

The people of Kivalina and the coastal tundra have a greater variety of materials with which to make their clothing than do those of the taiga or the inland tundra. Although the coastal people have sea-animal skins to use, they prefer the caribou for certain articles. Caribou calf

A summer tent village of fishermen from Noatak

Wolverine ruff and wolf-head mittens provide extra warmth

skins are used for parkas, pants, socks, and mittens because the hair is short and does not fall out. The fur of the wolverine is preferred as a ruff around the hood of a parka. One problem in the winter is that moist breath turns to frost and ice when it hits the edge of the hood, but this does not happen when moist breath hits the wolverine hair pulled across the face for protection.

The Eskimo mukluk (boot) has soles made from the skin of the hair seal and caribou skin uppers. Throughout their history Eskimos have used caribou sinew to sew up mukluks and skins, the Kivalina people now prefer to use dental floss. It is a bit disappointing to hear such a thing, but that is the way things are going. During the summer the Kivalina area people are most apt to wear white man's clothing. Teenagers, in particular, wear jeans and plaid shirts. They realize these are better for summer living, whereas their own homemade skin clothing is better in winter. The most-read books during the long winters are mail-order catalogues, such as *Sears* and *Wards*. The older people of the area learn more about the southern 49 states by reading and re-reading these colorful catalogues than by any other means.

FUEL

The Eskimos who live in the southern parts of the Kivalina area are very fortunate in having white spruce trees growing nearby. The United States Government allows them to cut wood for free if the wood is for their personal use. Only

An Eskimo woman making mukluks

one family in the village of Noatak uses an oil stove. Everyone else makes their stoves of empty oil drums which work very well and are inexpensive. A few sticks of dry wood will heat an entire hut in a matter of minutes and green wood will burn slowly all evening.

Although the stoves work well, the average family will burn up to 20 cords of wood per year, which would be a pile of 4-foot lengths of wood, 8 feet long by 80 feet high! Cutting wood and hauling it to the village, or floating it down the river, uses up a good part of a man's life. Usually a man will hunt animals while hunting wood in order to make the best use of his time and energy.

The problem of the Noatak men is small compared to the time and energy that must be spent by the Kivalina men. There is nothing but willow bushes along the Wulik and Kivalina Rivers. Wood gathering never ceases for these people and usually means a 25-to-50-mile round-trip along the beaches and up the rivers piling driftwood onto dog sleds and cutting green willows. During the cold winter a family will burn almost a sled-load per day.

The Kivalina people are truly happy when a seal, walrus, or whale is caught. The blubber can be used for fuel, thereby stretching the wood supply for a few weeks. When blubber is burned alone, it is done in the following way. A No. 10 can (about the size of a 2-pound coffee can) is punched full of holes on the top and sides. The side holes are for air, but the top holes allow melted blubber to fall through and catch fire. A handsized chunk of blubber has to be put on top of the can every few minutes because this little stove will burn up to 40 pounds of blubber per day.

Many Eskimos enjoy looking through mail-order catalogs

Usually the blubber and wood are burned together, thus using only about 10 pounds of blubber a day.

COMMUNICATIONS

There is not too much need for elaborate systems of communication and very few systems are available in the Kivalina area. There is no telephone, newspaper, radio, or television service locally. In a village like Kivalina many people have short-wave receivers that pick up Fairbanks, Anchorage, and Tokyo. Most small villages, however, do not have a radio transmitter with which to contact the outside in an emergency. Here, as in subarctic Canada, important personal messages are read over the nearest radio station. The message is then passed by word-of-mouth out to the isolated villages or homes. It may be days or weeks before someone is "going that way," but the message finally gets through. Once in a while a bush pilot will drop a message tied to a rock or a wrench as he passes over some isolated cabin.

A favorite form of recreation is to listen to all the personal messages as they are passed over the radio. Most messages have to do with Eskimos who are "outside" in tuberculosis or other hospitals and those who are "outside" going to school.

Noatak and Point Hope now receive communications

Umiak equipped with an outboard motor

and mail from aircraft pilots who make about three flights in and out each week, weather permitting. Kivalina receives only an occasional aircraft visit, though a charter flight can be arranged from Kotzebue, Noatak, or Point Hope. Mail comes in by boat or by dog team and only infrequently. This may sound very inconvenient but these people are, for the most part, self-contained. They do not have any reason to communicate with people all over the state, the country, or the world. Their world is small enough to be reached by sledding, kayaking, or shouting. A good communication system is needed most by a people in a hurry. The Eskimos, as well as anyone else who lives on the frontier fringes of the world, are used to waiting. They are usually tied so closely to nature that they have to be patient. They cannot change the wind direction in order to move the ice away. They cannot make the caribou migrate earlier than the caribou wish to. The whale will come close to the hunters on the ice—or he will not. One must simply wait. If the plane from Kotzebue does not come with the doctor today, it will probably come tomorrow, or the next day.

TRANSPORTATION

The people of Kivalina, Point Hope, and other villages along the coast travel by rowboat in the summer. Many of these boats are outfitted with large oil drums with which fresh water is collected at the mouth of the Wulik. Most summer travel on land is by foot.

Large skin boats, umiaks (oo-me-yaks), are used for spring seal hunting, fishing, and the never-ending job of collecting driftwood along the coast of the Chukchi. These

Kayak used for winter hunting

large boats, covered with the skin from eight bearded seals, can carry up to 3 tons, the weight of two or three automobiles. Since 1950 the Eskimos have been using outboard motors on the umiaks, usually of the 18-horsepower variety.

Kayaks are very small, one-man skinboats used mostly for winter hunting. Actually, the hunting is done by men standing on the ice pack. After an animal has been shot in the open water, one man shoves a kayak off the ice and paddles off after the animal and tows it back to the crowd. Many men and boys are camped on the pack ice for days at a time during hunting season, having brought their kayaks and tents out on dog sleds. The noisy dogs, children, and women pitch camp on the ice far back from the open water where the hunters are silently poised for striking.

The dog teams are the most important means of transportation. Their importance is partly shown by the fact that a village of 150 people will have about 175 working dogs, plus puppies and old dogs. This many dogs will eat as much as 500 pounds of food every winter's day—and all this food must be hunted by the human part of the ecosystem. The dogs are always fed, even when human starvation lurks. The people know that their only hope of avoiding starvation is to have dogs strong enough to go on long, hard, hunting trips. Only rarely have things gotten so bad that the dogs are starved, or eaten by the humans. They do not treat their sled dogs as lovable pets, but neither do they mistreat them.

A special kind of sled trail found along the coast of the Chukchi is the Kaimoo (kay-moo). The waves that come sliding up over the beach gravels in October leave a thin

Dog teams are vital to the Eskimos' survival

Sled dogs

layer of smooth ice each time. The sea is not cold enough to freeze yet, but these thin layers of water freeze on contact with the freezing air. The result of wave after wave, each depositing a thin layer of ice, is a three-foot-high embankment of ice along the beach. Sleds can move along its smooth top as though it were a highway.

COMMERCE AND INDUSTRY

Accompanying the absence of major transportation systems is a minimum of commerce. Although there is more commerce going on within the Kivalina area than in the Yana River area of Siberia, it is still nothing like what we would consider active commerce. The villages of Noatak, Kivalina, and Point Hope each has a store. Almost half of all the goods purchased from the Kivalina store are milk, coffee, sugar, flour, crackers, fruit, tea, butter, and jam. The remaining half are things like cigarettes, ammunition, cloth, dog harnesses, and Coleman gasoline lamps. In addition to this small amount of commerce, there are purchases made by mail from the well-thumbed mail-order catalogues. The average man, woman, and child in Kivalina spends about $250 a year between the store and the mail-order purchases. That small amount of money is for the purchase of food and clothing for the entire year. Everything else they need for survival is obtained by hunting and making things for themselves.

There is no activity within the Kivalina area that could be correctly called industry. One activity that might be called an industrial one is the *Caribou Hoof Jewelry Workshop.* This small workshop makes jewelry and such related things as buttons and buckles out of caribou hooves. Other tourist items such as sealskin moccasins, parkas, and children's Eskimo yo-yos are made at home and sold through the *Alaska Native Industries Cooperative Association* which assures the Eskimos of fair pay for their craft skills. These hand-crafted items are sold through hotel gift shops in Fairbanks, Anchorage, Juneau, Sitka, and Ketchikan, on the Alaska Ferry Boats, and at Alaskan airport waiting rooms where jet travelers from Asia, Europe, and North America cross paths on their great-circle routes.

GOVERNMENT AND SOCIETY

Although the Eskimos have been United States citizens ever since the purchase of Alaska from Russia in 1867, this did not affect their daily lives until recent years. For many Eskimos the first real contact with the outside world and their "fellow citizens" came with World War II when they were asked to join the U.S. Army and later when they were hired to build the DEW line radar sites and communication installations across Alaska and Canada. These contacts with "outsiders" began to change their lives and made them understand that they were now operating under the government of an unbelievably larger society.

Not too many government rules affected their daily lives at first. There were the occasional rules concerning the conservation of wildlife that concerned them directly, even though the regulations were aimed at white hunters and sportsmen. Since these people of the tundra only kill what they need there is little danger of their ruining the wildlife balance. They and the ecosystem of which they are a part are in balance.

The Eskimos of Alaska are now "looked after" by a number of governmental agencies. The United States Bureau of Indian Affairs helps them in various ways, including the operation of several schools to which Eskimos come from all over the state to learn trades that will help them earn money in the white man's world. There is some question about whether this is the best thing to do for the Eskimos. Some children, after being away from home so long while attending school, decide not to return to their old villages and old ways. Every time a strong, young boy decides not to return to Kivalina it is that much more difficult for the village hunters to supply meat and skins for everyone.

The United States Public Health Service also helps the Eskimos, particularly with tuberculosis hospitals, although tuberculosis has almost been beaten. The Alaska State Department of Health, Education, and Welfare also provides health care and operates such programs as Old Age Assistance, Aid to Dependent Children, and Aid to the Blind. People released from tuberculosis hospitals are not supposed to do hard work for 6 months, so the United States Bureau of Indian Affairs pays those in that situation.

Some people doubt that all this assistance is the best thing in the long run. The average citzen of Noatak, Kivalina, or Point Hope may receive as much as one-half of his annual dollar income from these various welfare agencies. A man's family may get more dollar income while he is away in the hospital than when he is home, healthy, and hunting.

The average citizen has little to say directly in the governmental activities just mentioned. He is more concerned with local, village government. The only form of government in Kivalina is the Village Council comprised of 7 village people. It is not as official as a town government, but it does establish certain rules of behavior. It is the group that deals with all the many outside agencies concerned with helping these 150 inhabitants of Kivalina. The council recently voted a small sales tax to be paid on anything sold at the village store. After they have enough money from this tax they plan to do something very useful for the village. They will buy a gasoline generator that will give them electricity.

There are several other elements in the social structure of Kivalina in addition to the Village Council. One of the most important is the Women's Club, which is formed both for recreation and for project work. The women are in charge of renting projectors and movie films from Anchorage for the weekly movie show. The profits are used to buy something for the village that the Council cannot or will not buy. Profits are also used to build up a fund from which families may borrow when they run short of dollars.

Kotzebue Hospital

National Guard Armory at Nome

A group of 5 women make up the Health Council. The Council is set up and trained by the United States Public Health Service to help the ill and the injured until the Nursing Service comes or the person is taken by boat or plane to the Kotzebue hospital.

About 9 of the Kivalina men belong to the National Guard Unit which has built a 20 by 60 foot building with its own heat and electricity. The armory is about the largest and most modern building in the village. The National Guard radio is always in contact with Nome, which can be a valuable service in a village emergency. The Guardsmen, who are paid by the United States Government, go to

Anchorage for a two-week training program once a year. The money received for this is extremely valuable to the men and their families.

The Friends and Episcopalian mission churches in Kivalina and Point Hope play important roles in the society, although less than in the earliest days of missionary work.

The school and its teacher play a very large part in the social structure of Kivalina, for almost everyone in the village realizes that the village leaders of tomorrow will come from those attending at least the 8 grades offered in Kivalina. The teacher at the village school is a very important person, for he or she is expected to know *everything.* The teacher sits in on the Council meetings; runs the clinic; handles the radio messages; makes breakfast for the students; and helps the Council as it deals with outside agencies.

As the Eskimos watch the teacher in his dealings with outsiders, in his paper form-filling, and his letter writing, they are beginning to realize how important such skills are and how powerful become those Eskimos who learn them. This one realization is causing the greatest upset in the ecosystem that has so long been in balance.

The clever hunter and boat-handler was the "important" man of the community—one to whose advice everyone listened. Young men would practice and practice at becoming great hunters to whom people paid respect. Young men of the village today are not practicing the art of hunting as hard because it is no longer the great hunter to whom people listen. Instead, it is the man who can "deal" best with the white man and his paper work. The communicator is now the "big man."

The white man's idea of who was "important" changed from the hunter to the pencil pusher over a period of several thousand years. The Eskimo's idea is changing in a very short time, and it makes life difficult for all concerned. Should other Americans help, almost force, the hunter to become a pencil pusher? Or should the Eskimo be encouraged to retain his more primitive life? He wonders whether it is better for his family and village if he goes outside and sends back dollars, washing machines, and radios, or if he stays home and hunts like his father before him. The answer is not simple and no one knows, for certain, what to do.

Eskimo children study at the village school

WORLD AREAS OF ICE CAP AND POLAR PACK
ATLANTIC OCEAN
NEWFOUNDLAND
HUDSON BAY
Fort Churchill
Churchill River
CANADA
BAFFIN ISLAND
DAVIS STRAIT
ICE CAP
GREENLAND
ICELAND
ARCTIC CIRCLE
66⅔°
NORTH SEA
Bergen
NORWAY
SWEDEN
FINLAND
Archangel
ELLESMERE ISLAND
SPITZBERGEN ISLANDS
NORTH POLE
FRANZ JOSEF LAND
POLAR PACK
ARCTIC OCEAN
NOVAYA ZEMLYA
OSTROV OKTYABARSKOY REVOLYUTSII
TUNDRA ANALOG AREA
CHUKCHI SEA
WRANGEL ISLAND
YUKON TERRITORY
Juneau
Fort Yukon
Yukon River
ARCTIC SLOPE
Barrow
Fairbanks
Nenana
Anchorage
KENAI PENINSULA
ALASKA
Kivalina
Kotzebue
Nome
CHUKCHI PENINSULA
Ob River
Dudinka
Norilsk
Igarka
Yenisei River
LAPTEV SEA
NEW SIBERIAN ISLANDS
SOVIET UNION
Lena River
TAIGA ANALOG AREA
Verkhoyansk
VERKHOYANSKI KHREBET
CHERSKI KHREBET
BERING SEA
Yakutsk
Magadan
LAKE BAIKAL
KAMCHATKA PENINSULA
SEA OF OKHOTSK
SAKHALINE ISLAND
PACIFIC OCEAN

CAP AND PACK

There are Arctic areas—very different from the taiga and the tundra—where man cannot become a natural part of the existing ecosystem. He occasionally enters the system, but ecologically he does not belong there and cannot survive without bringing artificial ecosystems with him.

Two such areas are called the *ice cap* and the *polar pack.* Man is intellectually interested in these regons and enjoys exploring them, but he always goes home. No man has ever lived his whole life on the cap or in the pack.

ICE CAP

The ice cap type of Arctic exists on islands surrounding the north polar region. By far the largest cap covers the immense island of Greenland, but large sections of Iceland, Ellesmere Island, and Baffin Island are also covered by caps of ice. Other caps are found on the islands of Spitzbergen, north of Norway. The Soviet Union has a few ice-capped islands: Franz Josef Land, Novaya Zemlya, and Ostrov Oktyabarskoy Revolyutsii (Islands of the October Revolution).

In thinking about the size of Greenland's ice cap, it helps

to picture Greenland lying over the United States. Its 840,000 square miles make it the world's largest island. If its east coast were laid over the east coast of the United States, its northern tip would be at the top of Maine and its southern tip would lie in the sea somewhere between Miami and Cuba. Greenland's west coast would lie, more or less, along the Mississippi River. Because of its vast size, very little is known about this island, the majority of which is covered by thousands of feet of ice and snow. All other ice caps in the world are tiny by comparison; except, of course, for the Antarctic cap, which is as large as the combined areas of the United States of America and Europe.

Snowfall is very light on this polar desert and seldom exceeds 6 inches per year. The only reason there is such a deep accumulation of snow is that almost none of it melts. For many thousands of years 6 inches have been piling up every year, and the depth of this snow and the resulting ice now amounts to 10,000 feet and more.

By mid-June summer comes to the Greenland plateau and temperatures zoom up to 15 and 25 degrees Fahrenheit. June evenings are cool, however, and drop to 5 degrees above zero. On really hot July days the temperature may go above 32 degrees Fahrenheit and melt some of the snow and ice, but these days are rare in the interior. Explorers, tired as they are of the winter, do not particularly like very warm days. The melted ice forms small streams and rivers that flow and erode beds where the explorers have to cross with their sleds or tracked vehicles. Wading across icy streams and then up through snowy drifts at temperatures hovering around freezing is not the best of all possible worlds. Most explorers prefer comfortable air temperatures just below freezing, when travel is almost as easy as in winter. By comparison, these temperatures really do feel comfortably warm to men who have grown accustomed to weather as much as 100 degrees colder.

Men explore the ice-cap environments of the world for many reasons, but one of the more important ones is to study ice and snow formations present there in permanent abundance. Many men have been fascinated with the process by which a delicate, lacelike snowflake becomes part of a monstrous, moving mountain of ice that rips apart rocks, gouges out fjords, and changes the face of a continent. Some of these men study to become glaciologists and spend many months of their lives climbing over, digging into, and living upon the objects of their fascination—ice caps and glaciers.

An ice cap—or, as it is sometimes called, an *ice sheet*—is a very broad area of deep snow and ice, usually found on highland areas. It covers peaks and valleys alike, but leaves occasional "islands" of rock, called *nunataks,* sticking up. The ice sheet flows outward from its center in all directions and spills over the mountain rim as *outlet glaciers* which become *valley glaciers* as the ice stream seeks out the lowest places along which to flow to the sea. It behaves, in this regard, like its more liquid ancestor, water.

If one were to sail northward through Greenland's Davis Strait and look up to the right to see some indication of an ice cap, he would see only indirect evidence that the center of this great island was an ice field. The evidence would be in the form of great numbers of large and small glaciers flowing slowly down to sea.

As snow accumulates at the head end of a valley it gradually changes in physical character. After a year or so snow begins to recrystallize until it resembles ice more than snow. During this period of change the snow is called *firn,* or *névè*, in French. After the annual layers of firn accumulate

An ice sheet spilling over to become glaciers

to a depth of about 200 feet, the firn has crystallized completely and is definitely ice, not snow. At some point in time enough weight of ice, firn, and snow has built up so that the pressure has caused the ice to flow like plastic. It flows in the same way that lava flows even after it appears to be solid rock. After the ice has started to move (and is thereafter known as a *glacier* and no longer a *snow field*), the friction of its motion across the rock creates enough heat to melt a very thin layer of ice at the bottom. This liquid lubricant allows the glacier to move more easily down hill (and even up hill) on its way to the sea.

When a glacier finally achieves its gravity controlled goal of sea level, it creates another display of both its beauty and its power. As the ice front pushes out to sea, it is attacked by the sea. Waves of warmer water smash and melt away a giant notch. When the overhanging weight is too great the front breaks off with a fearsome roar. A giant block of glacial ice crashes into the sea, producing a powerful wave that swamps any small craft in the vicinity.

Occasionally, the block of ice that was *below* the notch will then come seething up through the sea, bounding and rebounding like a gigantic blue cork until it finally settles down into a floating position. It then sails majestically after its upper half out through Davis Strait and down into the shipping lanes of the North Atlantic. This is how icebergs are born. For some reason, someone thought this birth of an iceberg resembled the birth of a calf and, ever since, this breaking off of many millions of pounds of ice has been called *calving*.

Many people have tried to figure out how much water

A floating glacial front from which bergs will calve

An iceberg moving south toward the Atlantic shipping lanes

would be produced if Greenland's ice cap were to melt. The best scientific estimate of its volume is 500,000 cubic miles, which if melted would raise the worldwide sea level about 21 feet. This would change the appearance of much of the world's shorelines and would flood such world population centers as London, Boston, New York, Buenos Aires, Rio de Janeiro, Calcutta, and Bombay. One has little to fear, however, because the best estimate is that it will take more than 10,000 years for it all to melt.

POLAR PACK

The polar pack is a massive expanse of floating ice that, even at its smallest size, covers an area four times greater than the Greenland ice cap. The North Pole is under a huge polar pack that extends from northern Greenland for hundreds of miles.

During the winter, after new ice has formed on the bottom of this gigantic ice raft, it is 8 to 12 feet thick. Summer melting reduces this to about 6 feet thick and about half as large.

By August, Greenland's coastal waters run free of solid ice, except for the extreme northern limits. The Gulf Stream and the North Atlantic Drift melt the pack back to the latitude of Spitzbergen, and open up sea lanes to ordinary ships bound for northern Norway, Sweden, and the Archangel port of Russia. The Bering Sea and the Chukchi Sea are free of ice by late July and August so that supply ships can reach Barrow and other northern Alaskan villages for their yearly visit. The supply ships usually have a doctor and dentist aboard to take care of all the illnesses saved up since the previous summer. Hudson Bay, Canada, is clear of ice from about July 1 to about October 1, during which period ships move western Canada's wheat from the great elevators at Churchill, Manitoba. The Sea of Okhotsk (awk-awtsk), north of Japan between the Kamchatka Peninsula and Siberia, opens for several summer months to enable ships to resupply such Siberian ports as Magadan.

Icebreakers, including the large atomic-powered *Lenin*, keep ships moving through the pack during the summer months along the northern coast of Siberia. This Northern Sea Route is necessary for Soviet defense in the Arctic, but it is a very difficult, dangerous, and expensive endeavor, just to serve the relatively few small settlements along the Arctic coast.

Although climatologists do not have much data, their best estimate of the North Pole temperatures during the year resemble this chart:

	J	F	M	A	M	J
°F	−42	−42	−31	−18	9	28

J	A	S	O	N	D	Annual Average
30	27	9	−11	−27	−36	−9°

It is even more difficult to estimate annual precipitation, but all climatologists agree that there is less than 10 inches, giving rise to the expression "the polar desert." All of whatever precipitation occurs falls as hard, granular snow. Although there may be an occasional blizzard, the central polar area is most apt to be clear and calm. At the pole itself there are 6 months of night and 6 months of day.

Until recently, most of man's knowledge of the polar pack came from early explorers who were trying to find a new way of getting around the Western Hemisphere rather than the long, expensive way around Cape Horn, Chile. They called this passage, which they never found, the Northwest Passage. Later, in the late 1800's, men began exploring for the sake of exploring and there are many books that tell exciting stories of such arctic explorers as Nansen, Sir Hubert Wilkins, Amundsen, Peary, and Stefánsson.

One of the first things these early exporers learned was that the polar pack is not one continuous, monotonously flat, sheet of ice. It is moving and changing continuously, summer and winter. Currents and winds are always at work, ripping the ice into large chunks, or *floes.* As these huge floes, sometimes several miles across, smash into one another the sounds can be heard for great distances as the edges get ground up and piled in grotesque heaps. These *pressure ridges* make travel across the polar pack extremely difficult. Even more difficult for the foot traveler are the *leads* of open water between the floes. Unless a man has a kayak along, it is not easy for him to get himself, his small sledge, and his dogs across even a few yards of freezing

Summer's open pack floats southward

cold water. The explorers who tried to get to the pole always went in winter when there are far fewer leads to worry about.

A modern icebreaker smashes its way by ramming at the edge of the pack until the ship's curved bow slides right up on the ice. After enough of the heavy ship is on top of the ice, the ice fails and breaks. The captain then

Close pack must be rammed and cracked

"backs her down" and rams it again to break up more of the pack. Sometimes the ship may get caught on top of the ice and be unable to go forward or backward. When this embarrassing state of affairs occurs, the captain gives the orders to *sally the ship*. The crew starts several huge pumps that pump liquid from tanks on the starboard side rapidly over to tanks on the port side. Then the direction is reversed, giving the ship a slow rocking motion that usually manages to break the ice.

If the pack cannot be worked by ramming, it is worked by *slewing*. The captain, using the reports from his "eyes" up in a helicopter, finds leads and noses the ship into one. As he forces the floes apart by pushing the engines "ahead full," he is said to be slewing. If the ship can neither break nor slew its way through and gets frozen in, it is said to be *beset*. Usually a captain would rather die than become beset, but there has been at least one ship intentionally beset in the polar pack—for science.

In 1879 the *Jeannette* was accidentally beset in the Chukchi Sea, near Wrangel Island. Four years later articles from the eventually crushed ship were found on a floe off the southern tip of Greenland. The great Norwegian scientist and explorer, Fridtjof (Fridge-off) Nansen heard of this and guessed that the polar pack drifts eastward, perhaps even across the pole itself. He took his ship, the *Fram*, and intentionally beset her in the polar pack north of the New Siberian Islands. He intended to get to the pole the "easy" way by drifting within the comparative comfort of the *Fram*, over the pole, and out into the open waters between Spitzbergen and Greenland. His ship, as predicted, did emerge from the pack there, three years later, but Captain Nansen did not. He walked home.

When Captain Nansen and Lieutenant Johansen realized that the *Fram* was not going to drift exactly over the pole they left the ship and tried for 28 days to sled to the pole. The two men came within 225 miles but had to turn back because they encountered too many open leads. They then hiked across the pack ice to Franz Joseph Archipelago, reaching there 5 months after leaving the ship, and after eating all but 5 of their dogs. After 9 winter months living in a sod hut, they made their way westward along the Siberian coast until they were picked up by a mapping expedition. The men from the *Fram,* believing their leaders dead, arrived in Bergen, Norway, only to be met on the dock by Nansen and Johansen.

There have been a number of fearless explorers such as Nansen, but because they had to spend most of their time surviving the rigors of life on the polar pack, there was little time left for scientific studies. There are plenty of scientists today interested in studying the Arctic Ocean environment, but until recently there had been no way for them to set up laboratories and living quarters within the pack. Then Colonel Fletcher of the U. S. Air Force noticed that a radar "target" that had been identified as an island was moving.

Ellesmere Island, the tenth largest island in the world, is one of the very few Arctic lands from whose glaciers icebergs are calved directly into the polar pack. Several of these glaciers on Ellesmere join hands as they reach the sea and float on as a wide *ice shelf,* still attached by icy apron strings to the mother glaciers. Occasionally a great section of this shelf will break off and float away as a *tabular berg.*

Because these tabular bergs may be as large as several hundred square miles in area and several hundred feet thick, they have been mistaken for and mapped as islands. Recently, these *ice islands* have become rather famous. The Soviet Union and the United States have recognized that they make excellent, floating scientific laboratories. Aircraft land and set up buildings, laboratories, and supply facilities for scientists who live and study on these floating platforms as they drift all over the Arctic Ocean, as much as a thousand miles per year. The Soviets call their stations North Pole One, North Pole Two, and so on, while we call ours T-1, T-2, T-3 (T for target) or ARLIS-I, ARLIS-II, and so forth (*A*rctic *R*esearch *L*aboratory *I*ce *S*tation I). These floating scientists are studying ice formation, ice freezing and melting processes, marine animal life, marine water, ocean bottom, and ocean currents. The ice islands are very strong and should enable these men to safely continue their work for years to come.

The Bering Strait, through which waters of the Pacific flow into the Arctic Ocean, is one of the shallowest parts of the World Ocean. The entire Chukchi Sea bottom is extremely level and never much deeper than 180 feet, and frequently shallower. The level bottom is the *continental shelf,* which also extends several hundred miles out from the Siberian shore.

When the now famous submarines *Nautilus* and *Skate* began studying the bottom of the Arctic Ocean prior to their making the under-the-pole dash, there was little known about the floor of this rather large ocean. Scientists knew only that there was a deep drop beyond the continental shelf. The studies by these submarines and their scientific friends floating above them on their ice islands have now produced a rather clear picture of the unusual sea floor.

The submarine *Nautilus* had difficulty finding a place off the coast of Alaska deep enough to submerge and still be certain that no unusually thick ice floes would smash its conning tower. Since the *Nautilus* itself is about 40 feet tall and since some floes are thicker than 100 feet, a sub-skipper hesitates to take his boat down in less than 200 feet of water. The *Nautilus* found a canyon off the coast of Barrow, Alaska, and followed it out into a deeper and deeper zone called the Canada Deep (over 12,000 feet deep); then up over Alpha Ridge (6,000 feet tall); then across the Markarov Deep (over 12,000 feet deep); up over the Tomonosov Ridge (6,000 feet tall); then across the safe depths of the Eurasia Deep; and out into the ice-free Lena Trough, between Spitzbergen and Greenland.

Commander William R. Anderson, USN, who skippered the *U.S.S. Nautilus* when she made her first transpolar run below the polar pack, is convinced that this is a fast and safe route for shipping between the Pacific and the Atlantic. Nuclear powered submarines, like the *Nautilus,* must be used because they do not need to surface for air or battery recharge. The ice would often make surfacing impossible, especially in late winter.

Shipping companies try all kinds of time-saving tricks in ordinary ocean crossings because they make more money on quicker runs. By this route across the Arctic they could cut as much as 5,000 miles from a normally 11,000 mile trip from Japan to England.

Aside from its economic value in terms of transportation, it is very important that scientists continue their studies of the polar pack and the Arctic Ocean for other reasons as well. Most important, perhaps, is that this vast expanse of water and ice affects the climate of the rest of the world.

When more is known about the day-to-day weather of the ice pack, weather conditions, especially in the northern hemisphere, can be predicted with greater accuracy. A rise of only 1 or 2 degrees in the average yearly temperature would melt so much pack ice that the level of the World Ocean would swell enough to flood coastal cities like New York and San Francisco. It would also increase the rainfall everywhere. Clearly, any change in climate would throw ecosystems out of balance throughout the world, and the people in the land of the hibernating rivers would have to adapt to a different way of life.